ASTERN BUSINESS

All ships get a good start in life!

ASTERN BUSINESS

75 Years of U.K. Shipbuilding

by

GEORGE H. PARKER

WORLD SHIP SOCIETY
1996

Also by the same author:

AT THE SHARP END!
(A Shipbuilding Autobiography)

ISBN 0 905617 80 0

© 1996 George H. Parker

Published by the World Ship Society
28 Natland Road, Kendal LA9 7LT England
1996

Printed by William Gibbons & Sons Ltd.,
Wolverhampton, England

ACKNOWLEDGEMENTS

I would like to place on record the great assistance I have received from various people in the production of this book. I would therefore express my sincere thanks to the following:

Firstly, to my wife, who, having quickly mastered a recently-acquired word processor, was readily able to accommodate my numerous alterations without complaint.

Secondly, to my brother, Cameron, who read the manuscript on a number of occasions and made various valuable suggestions and corrections.

Thirdly, to Reg Arnell, lately Board Member of Finance for British Shipbuilders, who supplied me with a number of documents relating to British Shipbuilders.

Fourthly, to Michael Crowdy, founder of the World Ship Society and his colleague David Burrell, who between them tactfully pointed out grammatical errors and suggested inclusion of certain facts previously unknown to me.

Fifthly, to Exeter University for permission to use their Library for purposes of research.

Finally, to the following for permission to reproduce the photographs and in respect of Appendices II, III, IV and V
Caledonian Newspapers Ltd.
John Brown Engineering Ltd.
J. D. Forbes
John G. McCulley
Turners (Photography) Ltd.
"Sunderland Echo"
Swan Hunter (Tyneside) Ltd.
World Ship Society
Photographers as individually acknowledged

George H. Parker,
Bampton, Devon
30th December 1995

CONTENTS

INTRODUCTION

There must be many people and I count myself among them, who are dismayed by the extent to which Britain's industrial base has shrunk, especially over the past two decades. The country now seems characterised by light engineering, electronics, information technology, financial services, consultants and analysts, tourism, museums and theme parks. This concoction offers little hope for those made unemployed by the near extinction of the coal and shipbuilding industries and the massive reductions of manpower in the heavy engineering and steel industries.

Some regard these changes as inevitable and coal and shipbuilding as "sundown" industries. But are they? It will surely be many decades yet before monster jet planes are able to transport huge cargoes of oil, grain, containers and the like across the world. Only ships can do this.

Others, while acknowledging that for the foreseeable future ships will be required, are resigned to a significant proportion being constructed in the Far East. They point to the comparatively low wages paid to South Korean workers for example and contrast this with U.K. wage rates, by way of justifying their view. If this were so, the German shipbuilding industry would be even more run-down than ours because their wages are considerably higher than British wages. On the contrary, the German shipbuilding industry is in reasonable shape. Although amalgamation, restructuring and redundancies have taken place, Germany is still a significant force in the world of shipbuilding.

One feature common to the U.K. coal, steel and shipbuilding industries was the fact that they were all nationalised. It was very nearly the end for British Steel and few would have rated their chances for a return to profitability after de-nationalisation. But in the end it prospered, although suffering a grievous loss of jobs in the process.

Following the year-long coal strike and the continuous restructuring of that industry, miners set new productivity records. British Coal however continued to close pits, claiming that demand could not match the current output. The playing field was by no means level however, since the issue was clouded by, first, imports of coal from around the world and, second, by privatisation of the Gas and Electricity industries. The fact that the handful of pits still in existence has been bought by private interests is surely proof that mines can be made to pay. And if this be so, why did Government not act sooner and allow more pits to be put up for sale, thus preserving employment?

Similar remarks apply to British Shipbuilders in the mid-80s. One yard after another was closed with few opportunities being available for private interests to purchase. Of course this would have required a radical overhaul of work practices as has already taken place in a privatised Scottish coalmine. The point is, the opportunity was denied by Government, bent on eliminating subsidies whatever the cost in unemployment.

Thus in 1995, little heavy industry is undertaken in Britain. It was a different story some seventy years ago.

British shipbuilding maintained its pre-eminent position in the world for almost a century. In 1948, its output still represented 51% of world output but this had plummeted to 5% by 1970. Although the real decline of this great industry took place between the late 50s and the late 80s, it is necessary to trace the U.K. shipbuilding industry's history from 1920 in order to comprehend the underlying reasons for it.

The methods of constructing steel ships had in 1920 changed little over a period of some 30 years. The gradual introduction of electric welding into the shipbuilding process was the catalyst for the great changes in hull construction which took place in the U.S.A., Sweden and elsewhere during World War II. Following the end of hostilities the badly damaged German and Japanese shipyards were rebuilt on modern lines and this was undertaken with American finance. The Swedes modernised their yards at the same time, all of them adopting the extensive use of electric welding and prefabrication of ships' structures.

For reasons explained later, U.K. shipbuilders were very late in modernising their facilities although the need for modernisation was not questioned. By the time that the first of the U.K. yards had been modernised, our main competitors, Sweden, Germany and Japan, had a 10 year start. During this crucial period between the late 40s and the late 50s, industrial relations in British shipbuilding steadily deteriorated and the industry was bedevilled by strikes, demarcation disputes and other forms of industrial action.

By the early 60s, U.K. yards had modernised to one extent or another. It was at this point that a sudden collapse occurred in freight rates resulting in an order famine. This caused a number of U.K. yards to go out of business. Those that remained found the competition even tougher and this was not helped by ever-increasing labour unrest and strife. This was the start of the serious decline of the industry.

Prior to modernisation, the situation was one in which the plant and machinery were basic and the work depended largely on the craftsman's skills. The shipbuilding centres of the U.K. were abundant sources of skilled labour and in boom times additional skilled labour could be immediately employed with minimum impact upon overheads, due to the comparatively low investment in shipyard facilities.

This was not the case in western Europe, for example, where skilled labour was in short supply for shipbuilding. This is one reason why, immediately after World War II, shipbuilders in those countries invested in the new technology which involved welding, prefabrication and the use of automated marking, burning and welding machines. These machines were designed to be operated by semi-skilled operatives.

These fundamental changes to shipbuilding construction technology killed at a stroke the need for the high skills inherent in the boilermaker trades. No longer did Britain enjoy the advantages of these skills over its competitors.

Worse than this was the fact that when, ten years later, U.K. yards installed this equipment, the boilermakers insisted that their skilled members had the sole right to operate the plant which had taken the place of these same skills. The fact that the machines could be operated by semi or even unskilled operatives cut no ice with the boilermakers and in many cases these machines were not only "overskilled" but also overmanned, rendering U.K. shipbuilding uncompetitive.

Due to the continuing decline in productivity, combined with the overmanning of new plant and the added cost of demarcation, it is difficult to see in retrospect, with a few notable exceptions, any improvement in cost and in construction times due to the investment in expensive new plant in U.K. yards.

Of course it is true that as new types of ships made their appearance in the 50s and 60s their steel structures were more complex. Even a plain bulk carrier of the 50s had a more complex steel structure than that of the pre-war cargo tramp which it had replaced. Thus comparisons of cost and building times can be misleading. This is to ignore, however the comparative simplicity that the wide use of electric welding brought to the hull construction process.

Before World War II, during wartime and for some ten years or so thereafter, the industry had no equal. Despite the elderly equipment and poor craneage, some remarkable building times were achieved. The progress photographs of S.S. EMPIRE HEYWOOD, which form Appendix I, record the astounding speed of construction of a wartime standard ship built by the Caledon Shipbuilding & Engineering Co. Ltd., at Dundee. After its launch on the 21st October 1941, the ship was delivered on 31st December 1941. It should be noted that the five other shipbuilding berths were all occupied and with labour committed to them. This level of productivity was by no means untypical of these times.

One notable factor absent from much of what has already been written about the industry is the profit motive. As with any business, this has to be the prime consideration. Yet one of the reasons advanced by some for the industry's decline is that it, or more properly its owners, failed to expand its output during the period in the 50s and 60s when world demand for ships rose so spectacularly. The reality, of course, was that our many competitors who did expand their output found that their financial results were little better than ours.

It is, needless to say, impossible to forecast future supply and demand with any degree of accuracy. Our European competitors took the view that world demand for ships would continue to increase, or at any rate remain at the high level reached at that time. They could not have foreseen the oil crisis in 1973, followed by the collapse of freight rates a year or so later. Still less, perhaps, could they have foreseen the further expansion in world shipbuilding that would shortly take place. No blame attaches to them for expanding their facilities, but as things turned out it was "profitless prosperity".

The British shipbuilder by contrast was cautious, probably too cautious. Certainly we were late in modernising our shipyards compared to our

9

competitors, although many had not the financial resources to undertake costly improvements. The caution displayed by the British shipbuilder was born of experience—experience in the cauldron of two depressions, not suffered by all of our competitors.

This experience was also a factor in the industry's dealings with the trade unions. While it is true that suspicion and mistrust characterised this relationship for a century or more, the proposition that 'third parties' were required to break the deadlock can be readily refuted by referring to examples of such intervention by outsiders to the industry. Attempts to improve productivity at Fairfields (Glasgow) Ltd. in 1965 for example were not proved. Indeed it appears that productivity bonuses may have been paid in advance of their achievement. Possibly a bit of suspicion on the part of its management might have paid more dividends! The same goes for Upper Clyde Shipbuilders and later for British Shipbuilders.

This is not to say that the traditional British shipbuilder had no faults, committed no errors of judgement and was not in any way responsible for the industry's decline. But if the above examples of management consultants and industrial relations experts brought in to advise, and in some cases to occupy positions of executive authority, are anything to go by, then in many cases their performance fell short of that of the professional shipbuilder.

A further reason advanced by some for the industry's decline was lack of specialisation in a particular product. The merits of series production using capital-intensive facilities had been overlooked by most of the U.K. yards, or so it is alleged. Some others have suggested that, following modernisation of U.K. shipyards in the late 50s and early 60s, appropriate planning techniques were not introduced for the purpose of production control. In steelwork manufacture, the substitution of a plater's individual skills by a numerically-controlled automatic burning machine lends itself to a system of planning controls. So too does the next few sequences in steel fabrication—viz. the joining of flat plates into panels by automatic welding machines followed by the positioning and welding of stiffeners, again by automatic machines. But all the subsequent processes—assembly into three-dimensional units, further assembly into large block units, erecting and fairing on the berth, all involve operatives working in confined spaces and much of the work is positional, as distinct from flat work. Such work is difficult to plan on a systematic basis.

A potted history of the industry from 1920 to 1939 may indicate why British shipbuilders were driven to the conclusion that product variety was the safest course. What transpired after the late 50s is a different story, although it is ironic to note that in the mid 90s the merits of product variety are once again being appreciated.

This book is concerned only with builders of ships exceeding around 5,000 tons deadweight. The smaller shipbuilders were, for the most part, operating in different markets and were not nationalised in 1977.

LOCATION OF SHIPYARDS

Upper Clyde

Harland & Wolff Ltd.—Govan
Fairfield Shipbuilding & Engineering Co. Ltd. (later Govan Shipbuilders Ltd.)—Govan
Alex. Stephen & Sons Ltd.—Linthouse
Barclay, Curle & Co. Ltd.—Whiteinch
Chas. Connell & Co. Ltd.—Scotstoun
Blythswood Shipbuilding Co. Ltd.—Scotstoun
Yarrow & Co. Ltd.—Yoker
John Brown & Co. Ltd.—Clydebank
W. Beardmore & Co. Ltd.—Dalmuir

Lower Clyde

William Denny & Bros. Ltd.—Dumbarton
William Hamilton & Co. Ltd.—Port Glasgow
Lithgows Ltd.—Port Glasgow
The Greenock Dockyard Co. Ltd.—Greenock
Scotts' Shipbuilding & Engineering Co. Ltd.—Greenock

Tyne

Sir W. G. Armstrong, Whitworth & Co. Ltd. (later Vickers-Armstrongs Ltd.)—Walker
Swan, Hunter & Wigham Richardson Ltd. Neptune Yard—Walker
Swan, Hunter & Wigham Richardson Ltd. Wallsend Yard—Wallsend
R. & W. Hawthorn, Leslie & Co. Ltd.—Hebburn
Palmers' Shipbuilding & Iron Co. Ltd.—Jarrow
John Readhead & Sons Ltd.—South Shields

Wear

Short Bros. Ltd—Pallion
Wm. Doxford & Sons Ltd. (later Sunderland Shipbuilders Ltd.)—Pallion
William Pickersgill & Sons Ltd. (later Austin & Pickersgill Ltd.)—Southwick
Sir James Laing & Sons Ltd. (later Sunderland Shipbuilders Ltd.)—Deptford
J. L. Thompson & Sons Ltd. (later Sunderland Shipbuilders Ltd.)—North Sands
Bartram & Sons Ltd.—Sunderland Docks

Tees

Furness Shipbuilding Co. Ltd. (later Swan Hunter)—Haverton Hill
Smith's Dock Co. Ltd.—South Bank

Mersey

Cammell Laird & Co. Ltd.—Birkenhead

Barrow-in-Furness

Vickers-Armstrongs Ltd. (later Vickers Ltd.)

Belfast

Harland & Wolff Ltd.—Queens Island
Workman, Clark & Co. Ltd.—Queens Island

Outposts

Hall, Russell & Co. Ltd.—Aberdeen
Caledon Shipbuilding & Engineering Co. Ltd.—Dundee
Henry Robb Ltd.—Leith
Burntisland Shipbuilding Co. Ltd.—Burntisland
Blyth Shipbuilding & Dry Docks Co. Ltd.—Blyth
William Gray & Co. Ltd.—West Hartlepool
John I. Thornycroft & Co. Ltd.—Southampton
Appledore Shipbuilders Ltd. — Bideford

CHAPTER 1

BETWEEN THE WARS
1920-1939

Apart from 1920, when all yards were busy replacing war losses, the other 19 years of this period were to prove a mixed blessing for U.K. shipbuilders. The large yards for most of this period were at least working, but many of the other yards were either closed permanently or closed and re-opened as the market picked up.

Up to 1970 or thereby, the prosperity or otherwise of the U.K. shipbuilder was largely dependent upon the shipping market and foreign competition. The shipping market over this 50 year period was characterized by violent fluctuations, giving rise to the "hunger and burst" nature of the shipbuilding cycle. In 1920, U.K. shipbuilding accounted for about 60% of world shipbuilding output and so the foreign competition, although significant, did not then constitute the major factor in determining the U.K. shipbuilders' prosperity.

By the 1970s, the situation had radically changed, with U.K. shipbuilders accounting for less than 5% of world output while foreign governments as well as our own were subsidising their shipbuilding industries. Thus it came about that market forces alone did not dictate the fortunes of British shipbuilders.

In 1920 the industry employed in excess of 350,000 workers. The working week had been reduced from one of 54 hours to one of 47 hours in 1919. In 1920, the Clyde output alone was 672,438 gross tons. Much of this output was for U.K. account, where individual yards had established relationships with particular owners. These relationships were maintained through periods of depression and when the market recovered, further business was undertaken by the individual yard for the particular owner.

Contracts were placed on a cash basis and the price paid to the shipbuilder by instalments. These could vary to some extent but were normally paid at contract signing, on keel laying, on completion of framing, on completion of plating, at launch and on delivery. Frequently there was no contract—the price and delivery date being formalised by a handshake.

A wide variety of ships were constructed by British yards including warships, passenger liners, oil tankers and cargo vessels of various types together with a host of smaller vessels.

So far as naval output was concerned, 1920 saw the completion of the battle-cruiser H.M.S. HOOD from Clydebank. At 42,000 tons standard displacement and fitted with 8—15" guns and an array of lighter armaments, she was the largest, fastest and most powerful ship in the Royal Navy. Two cruisers —

H.M.S. FROBISHER and H.M.S. EMERALD were completed the same year together with two destroyers and three submarines.

All this was a far cry from the earlier years of the First World War when a huge naval building programme was undertaken, including battle-cruisers, battleships, aircraft carriers, cruisers, light cruisers, large numbers of destroyers and submarines.

Naval vessels both during and after the First World War were constructed not only by a number of large and medium-sized yards spread across the country but also by the Royal Naval Dockyards at Chatham, Devonport and Portsmouth.

The post-war boom was very short-lived, as wartime losses of merchant ships were quickly replaced utilising the huge potential of U.K. yards. The boom in warship building, noted above, came to an end at the same time. By mid-1920 world trade was falling, and the U.S.A. had become isolationist with millions of tons of laid-up war-built shipping. Much of Germany's shipping was taken over by the Allies as reparations and much of it sold by the British Government to U.K. owners just when the boom was ending. To make matters worse, the cost of materials, notably steel, had risen sharply and so too had wages. Owners began to cancel orders because of rising building costs combined with falling freight rates.

The position worsened in 1921 with more orders cancelled or suspended, while the Government continued to sell ex-enemy ships for half the cost of newbuildings. The trade slump continued for five long years up to 1926. During this period, unemployment in the industry was very high. In towns like Port Glasgow on the River Clyde and Sunderland on the River Wear, which relied heavily on the industry for their livelihood, these were particularly grim times. Shipbuilding output on the River Clyde, for example, fell from the 672,438 gross tons of 1920 to 179,529 tons in 1923. An even more severe drop was recorded on the River Wear, where output fell from 333,335 tons in 1920 to 56,522 tons in 1923.

In an effort to reduce overall building costs, shipbuilders cut wages. This action led to a number of damaging strikes, including the shipyard joiners strike which lasted from December 1920 until August 1921. The miners also went on strike from April until July 1921. This series of strikes of course reached its crescendo in the General Strike of 1926.

Limited use was made by British shipbuilders, notably Harland & Wolff, of the Trade Facility Acts (and Northern Ireland's Loans Guarantee Acts), to raise capital for modernisation. Many British and foreign owners also used the same vehicle to finance over one hundred ships in the 1920s, ranging up to liners such as CONTE VERDE, FRANCONIA, LETITIA and GEORGIC.

On 27th August 1923, Lord Inverforth wrote to the T.F.A. Committee— 'I have just come back from a visit to the River Clyde and am somewhat disturbed by the serious condition of unemployment'. To relieve this he ordered no less than nineteen ships from Harland & Wolff's Govan yard, delivered to the Bank Line between 1924 and 1926.

AGIOS SPYRIDON (Ex North Devon) of 3,653 gross tons built for North Shipping Co. Ltd. by John Readhead & Sons Ltd. in 1924. W.S.P.L.

BRITISH CHIVALRY of 7,118 gross tons built for the British Tanker Co. Ltd. by Palmers' Shipbuilding & Iron Co. Ltd. in 1929. W.S.P.L.

Over this five year period ending in 1926, a number of yards were closed and dismantled while others closed and re-opened some years later. A few shipbuilders undertook shipbreaking in an effort to find work for their beleaguered staff and employees. But some yards were harder hit than others during this period. In general, those in the habit of constructing tramp steamers and oil tankers fared worst, since such vessels were taking the brunt of the slump in world trade. The larger yards with experience of building naval ships and passenger liners fared better, although they were far from full of work.

The U.K. Government had intended to build no less than four battle-cruisers, but under the terms of the Washington Naval Treaty of 1922, this plan had to be abandoned. The Treaty was in fact signed by Britain, America and Japan and provided for parity in battleships between Britain and America with Japan accepting inferiority in the ratio 5: 5: 3 respectively. From 1920 to 1926, only four cruisers, eight destroyers and ten submarines were completed. Some relief came to yards on Tyneside and Merseyside in 1923 with the order to construct the battleships H.M.S. NELSON and H.M.S. RODNEY as allowed under the Treaty. Thus the majority of the large yards found no relief from the slump insofar as naval orders were concerned.

Armstrong, Whitworth of Walker on Tyne, prolific builders of major warships, got into financial difficulties in 1926. The business comprising shipbuilding and armaments was merged with Vickers of Barrow in 1927 to become Vickers-Armstrongs Ltd.

The acute shortage of naval work was compensated somewhat by passenger liner building. No less than fourteen passenger ships were delivered in 1925 alone. This work was not evenly spread across the large yards. Harland & Wolff. for example, built eighteen such vessels during the years 1921-1926. Other large yards were not so fortunate, although John Brown and Fairfield each had a fair share. Most of the famous U.K. shipping companies, together with a few foreign ones, figured in this spread of work—particularly P&O, Cunard and Union-Castle. The larger yards were also able to secure work for cross-Channel ferries and the occasional refrigerated cargo/passenger vessel, such specialised work being beyond the experience and capacity of the tramp builders.

In 1925, Prince Line ordered five ships to upgrade their round-the-world service. British shipbuilders were dismayed when the order was placed with German builders, the first major order placed abroad by British owners.

For the first time, the Shipbuilding Employers Federation and the Confederation of Shipbuilding and Engineering Unions joined forces in a Joint Committee of Enquiry, achieving a measure of unanimity not generally noted in the industry.

The years 1927/8/9 brought a little relief to the industry but it was to be only a respite. Only about half of the available building berths were in use during this period. But orders were placed and output rose and unemployment fell, even in the most depressed towns of Port Glasgow and Sunderland, wherein were concentrated the majority of the yards capable of building only cargo vessels, tramp steamers and oil tankers. A few yards laid down their standard ships "on spec".

The larger yards began to benefit from the naval programme which involved, in particular, cruisers. One cruiser was delivered in 1927, seven in 1928 (including two for the Royal Australian Navy) and four in 1929. The majority of this work concerned the famous three-funnelled heavy cruisers of the "London", "Kent" and "Norfolk" classes. The last two units were delivered in 1930.

Passenger liner building continued apace during this three year period with eight ships completed in 1927, five in 1928 and no less than twelve in 1929. As before, this work was not evenly spread, the main beneficiaries being John Brown (nine vessels) and Harland & Wolff (seven vessels).

In 1930, a slump of even greater severity than that of the mid-20s overtook the world economies. This slump began in the U.S.A. where a collapse of confidence in October 1929 effectively stopped the flow of American money. The primary producers, already impoverished, were impoverished still further. As a result they ceased to buy British goods and ceased to need the services of British ships. By 1931, the cost of imports had fallen and trade had turned in the U.K.'s favour. Wages had remained stable and with the fall in prices, real wages actually rose—that is, for those still in employment. Although this slump was world-wide and was to last for upwards of four years, unemployment in the U.K. as a whole was not as severe as in 1924. But it was far worse than before in the North, Scotland and South Wales — wherein were concentrated mining, steel-making and shipbuilding. By 1931, U.K. shipbuilding numbers had fallen to some 201,000, of whom over half were unemployed. Whereas the industry had a capacity of 3,000,000 gross tons a year at the end of the First World War, it had never since 1920 been called upon to produce much more than 1,500,000 tons. By 1930, it was not called upon to produce anything but a fraction of this.

NATIONAL SHIPBUILDERS SECURITY LTD.

The shipbuilders themselves decided to cut back the surplus capacity and thus avoid the heavy cost of maintaining surplus shipyards in idleness. Thus was formed in February 1930 National Shipbuilders Security Ltd., whose task was to buy out and thereafter close down and dismantle yards whose owners were prepared to sell out. Working capital was provided by the Bankers Industrial Development Company in the form of debentures, repaid by a levy of 1% raised on the price of vessels laid down after 1st November 1930, an initiative taken by the shipbuilders themselves. The chairman of the company was Sir James Lithgow and the directors were shipbuilders of yards located in a number of shipbuilding centres.

This process of rationalisation started at once and by 1936 no less than 184 building berths had been scrapped out of a total of 684 across the country. Those yards which accepted the terms of an N.S.S. offer, and these encompassed companies in many of the shipbuilding centres, appreciated that the terms of the offer precluded the building of ships on the site for a period of 40 years.

The cruiser H.M.S. SHROPSHIRE of 9,830 tons standard displacement built by William
Beardmore & Co. Ltd., in 1929.   W.S.P.L.

VICEROY OF INDIA — 19,648 gross tons passenger liner built for P&O's London to
Bombay service by Alexander Stephen & Sons Ltd., in 1929.   W.S.P.L.

The first yard to be sold to N.S.S. was that of Napier & Miller Ltd. of Old Kilpatrick on the Upper Clyde in 1930.

In 1930 British shipping was rocked by the collapse of the Royal Mail Group, headed by Lord Kylsant, with losses exceeding some £50 million. A major member of the Group was Harland & Wolff who only survived by capital re-structuring, effectively losing more than £12 million.

Of the four battle-cruiser orders that the Government had intended to place, one had been earmarked for Beardmores. The abandonment of this plan under the terms of the Washington Treaty almost certainly led to the yard's ultimate demise. The terms of the London Naval Treaty signed in 1930 obliged the three powers concerned—namely Britain, America and Japan—not to build any battleships until 1st January 1937. The terms of this Treaty only served to reinforce the decision to close Beardmores.

Many of those yards unwilling to accept an offer from National Shipbuilders Security were themselves closed through lack of work. Many yards on the Tyne and Wear fell into this category, as did some on the Clyde. The period of closure varied, but for some it was for six long years. Some kept on apprentices building ships "on spec", while Vickers-Armstrongs' Naval yard reopened briefly to construct a passenger liner, the MONARCH OF BERMUDA, only to close again when that ship was delivered.

The closure of a particular yard by National Shipbuilders Security was viewed by some at the time as damaging to the particular town in question. Many argued that in the future the nation might need the capacity now effectively sterilised and Town Councils and other authorities protested to the Government against the closures. The fact was, however, that after N.S.S. had closed its last yard in 1938, the industry still had a surplus of capacity right up to the outbreak of the Second World War, despite the improvement in shipbuilding's fortunes for the three years prior to 1939. Not surprisingly, large numbers of disillusioned workers sought work elsewhere during the period of the Great Depression, never to return to the industry. When war was declared, it was perfectly clear that the call for skilled men by the shipyards could not be met.

During 1930/31, negotiations were concluded between the Cunard Company and John Brown for the building of a super Atlantic liner, referred to as Yard No. 534. Some time after construction had commenced, the owners requested that the work be suspended. It was not to recommence until April 1934. During the first half of this period the yard was all but closed. In 1932, the West Yard at Clydebank was reopened following the Admiralty order for two sloops and two destroyers.

Meanwhile the Depression continued and N.S.S. bought and thereafter closed a number of smaller yards on the Clyde, the Tyne and the Wear between 1931 and 1935. Palmers of Jarrow on Tyneside, builders of major naval vessels, tankers and colliers were now bereft of work and with no prospect of obtaining any. It was in fact bankrupt and beyond hope of saving. It was acquired by

N.S.S. and closed in 1933. A storm of protest erupted, led by Jarrow' s M.P. Ellen Wilkinson but was of no avail.

As before, a number of the large yards were engaged in the construction of passenger liners. This work was by no means evenly spread across these yards. Some lovely ships were built during this period including the EMPRESS OF BRITAIN by John Brown in 1931. Five other liners were delivered the same year including the beautiful MONARCH OF BERMUDA from Vickers-Armstrongs' Naval yard and the STRATHNAVER from Vickers-Armstrongs' Barrow yard. The Barrow yard delivered the sister ships to these vessels— the STRATHAIRD in 1932 and the QUEEN OF BERMUDA in 1933.

After 1931, only Vickers-Armstrongs at Barrow was engaged in passenger work, apart from the completion of the GEORGIC at Belfast the following year. Thus, during the years 1931 to 1933, most of the large yards were as desperate for work as the rest of the merchant shipbuilders. Harland & Wolff of Belfast for example ran out of work at the beginning of 1932 and, after delivery of the M.V. GEORGIC in June of that year, this huge yard was placed on a care and maintenance basis. Work was not resumed until the autumn of 1933.

NAVAL PROGRAMME

Some relief was at hand in 1932/33 for builders of naval vessels, at least, when the Government announced that it intended to proceed with the naval programme which had been in abeyance. The two sloops and two destroyers ordered from John Brown were evidence of this, as were the orders placed for three cruisers of the "Arethusa" class (one with Chatham Naval Dockyard and one each with Scotts and Harland & Wolff). So, too, were orders placed for a large number of destroyers and submarines. The 1933 naval programme embraced orders for two cruisers of the "Southampton" class, together with further destroyers and submarines. The first of the destroyer class was ordered from John Brown and about the same time, news was received of a resumption of work on the giant Cunarder. This event gave rise to a feeling of renewed confidence in the economic future of the country.

During this period also, a proportion of U.K. shipping was laid up although at 17% the proportion was 3% less than that laid up during the 1920s slump. In 1933 world trade picked up, but the demand for ships was initially absorbed by ships taken out of lay-up and it was only by 1934 that freight rates began to inch upwards. The rise in freight rates had been delayed by operating subsidies for tramp shipping introduced by Italy in 1932, by Germany and Holland in 1933 and by France in 1934.

While these subsidies were adversely affecting U.K. owners, a number of countries had also introduced building subsidies in an attempt to assist their ailing shipbuilding industries. In 1932, for example, Japan introduced a subsidised "scrap and build" scheme complete with interest-free loans. And in the year following, Germany offered its shipowners a general operating bounty of 25% of operating costs. Italy too was offering subsidies.

Many yards in the U.K. benefited from the work stemming from the naval programmes of 1933 through to 1935, but these did not include the numerous shipyards with experience of building only cargo vessels and oil tankers. Such vessels were still not in demand and some of the yards in question had not built a single ship for five or six years. In 1935 N.S.S. bought the large shipyard of Workman, Clark in Belfast and it was thereafter closed.

It should be noted that the British Government, which was assisting other industries by tariffs, grants or subsidies, had not lifted a finger to assist either the shipping or shipbuilding industry during the economic blizzard that had engulfed them for upwards of four years. Both industries up to this point had operated in open competition with foreign fleets and yards despite the subsidies being enjoyed by some of their foreign competitors as noted above.

In an effort to revive the fortunes of both the U.K. shipping and shipbuilding industries, the government at long last introduced in 1935 a "scrap and build" scheme. Under this, Government loans were made available up to £10,000,000 at a fixed interest rate of 3% and repayable over twelve years to encourage owners to place orders for new ships in U.K. yards. The offer was made subject to owners agreeing to scrap two tons for every one ordered. The scheme had an immediate impact and before it ended a year later, fifty new ships had been ordered. Twenty-four of these were placed with yards on the Wear, one of the worst hit areas of the slump.

The shipbuilding and shiprepairing business of D. & W. Henderson & Co. Ltd., on the Upper Clyde was, due to the difficulty of obtaining orders, sold to N.S.S. in 1935. The shipyard built mainly cargo liners and tramps and counted prestigious names among its clients, including Anchor Line, Lamport & Holt, Leyland Line, T. & J. Harrison and Elder Dempster. The business had been bought by Harland & Wolff in 1917.

Shiprepairing continued until 1962 when the Govan yard of Harland & Wolff closed.

Caird & Co. Ltd., of Greenock, was also sold to N.S.S. in 1935. This long-established yard was also acquired by Harland & Wolff in 1916 and three years later the yard was extended and modernised. Among its distinguished customers were P&O for whom the company built the RAWALPINDI and the RAJPUTANA in 1925.

In 1935 also, the Fairfield yard at Govan got into financial difficulties and was only prevented from closure by the swift intervention of the Lithgow family who took over the majority of the ordinary shares.

The General Election of 1935 returned a Conservative Government to power. They were committed to a policy of re-armament. This policy was the result of the rapid expansion that was taking place in the navies of Italy, Germany and Japan. The terms of the London Naval Treaty expired on 1st January 1937 when the parties to the Treaty could, if they so wished, lay down battleships. From this point on, Britain pursued her avowed policy of re-armament with the utmost vigour. It was now recognised that efforts must be made to overtake the arrears of warship building which had accumulated during the Treaty years. The Treaty had imposed certain restrictions on the building of cruisers and in this area too, Britain prosecuted her re-armament policy with speed.

RE-ARMAMENT

The naval programme for 1936 included orders for the battleships KING GEORGE V and PRINCE OF WALES with Vickers-Armstrongs on Tyneside and with Cammell Laird at Birkenhead respectively. These ships would be laid down on 1st January 1937—the very date the Treaty expired. The programme also included orders for two cruisers of the improved "Southampton" class with Swan Hunter and Wigham Richardson on Tyneside and with Harland & Wolff at Belfast. In addition, five cruisers of the "Dido" class were ordered—one each with Cammell Laird, Scotts and Hawthorn Leslie and two with Chatham and Portsmouth Royal Dockyards. Two aircraft carriers were ordered—namely H.M.S. ILLUSTRIOUS and H.M.S. VICTORIOUS with Vickers-Armstrongs at Barrow and on Tyneside. A number of destroyers and submarines were also ordered.

In 1936, R.M.S. QUEEN MARY was delivered by John Brown. The construction of this magnificent vessel had given employment, not only to thousands of workers within the shipyard and engine works, but also to a host of suppliers and subcontractors. The ship entered service on the Atlantic and was an immediate success. Negotiations were in hand between owners and builders for the construction of a sister vessel.

TURNING POINT

1936 proved a turning point in the fortunes of U.K. shipbuilders. The re-armament programme already noted had started to transform the order books and employment prospects for the significant numbers of large, medium and small yards experienced in the construction of naval vessels. In this year also, a substantial improvement in shipping freight rates occurred and orders were placed with the beleaguered merchant shipbuilders. Later in the year, Cunard ordered the sister ship of QUEEN MARY at Clydebank.

The improvement in merchant shipping orders continued in 1937 and in the same year, the naval programme was even greater than that of the previous year. It included orders for three battleships of the "King George V" class—namely H.M.S. ANSON, H.M.S. JELLICOE and H.M.S. BEATTY, and these were placed with John Brown, Swan Hunter and Fairfield respectively. The programme also included two further aircraft carriers—H.M.S. FORMIDABLE with Harland & Wolff and H.M.S. INDOMITABLE with Vickers-Armstrongs at Barrow. In addition, orders for five cruisers of the "Fiji" class were placed with John Brown, Alexander Stephen, Swan Hunter, Vickers-Armstrongs at Newcastle and at Devonport Dockyard. Further orders were placed for two cruisers of the "Dido" class with Alexander Stephen and Scotts'. Further destroyer and submarine orders were placed, as were orders for two depot ships—one at Belfast and one at Clydebank.

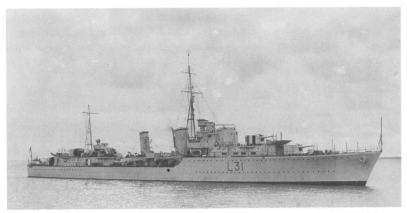

One of sixteen handsome Tribal Class destroyers — H.M.S. MOHAWK of 1,850 tons standard displacement and built by John I. Thornycroft & Co. Ltd., in 1938.
W.S.S. Blackman Collection

CAPETOWN CASTLE — 27,002 gross tons passenger liner built for the Union-Castle Mail Steamship Co. Ltd., by Harland & Wolff Ltd., in 1938.
W.S.P.L.

23

The large yards were now very busy executing naval and passenger ship contracts as were medium-sized yards with naval and intermediate passenger ships. The merchant shipyards were gradually filling with work. At this point, British shipbuilding output accounted for some 35% of the world output, as compared to around 60% in 1920. But the current figure was in respect of a much reduced total.

Shipping orders placed in 1937 resulted in output from the pure merchant yards a year later being the highest since 1930. But in 1938 orders became more difficult to obtain and as the end of the year approached, the employment situation was once again deteriorating. The reasons that orders became scarce were two-fold. First, the effects of the trade recession in the earlier months of the year were compounded by the international crisis and the level of shipbuilding prices. Second, of those orders that were placed, the majority were placed by U.K. owners at Continental yards, where considerable price savings were evident. For U.K. shipbuilders the result was that for every four vessels launched only one new ship was ordered. The price levels throughout the whole range of the supply industries were higher than in a number of competing countries and it was this factor which was largely responsible for the high prices of U.K.-built ships.

By the end of 1938 and despite the huge increase in warship work and the elimination of around one-third of the berths in this country by N.S.S., only 45% of the existing berths were occupied. This percentage is less than that applying when N.S.S. began its operations. Without the naval contracts, of course, many yards would have been very short of work.

Although, as has been noted above, the U.K. yards' output for 1938 was the highest since 1930, foreign competition had become a real threat. Typical was Germany. Foreign companies could not remit profits abroad, but could build and export ships for sale. Unilever for example, placed sixty-eight orders between 1934 and 1936. Germany also bartered ships for whale oil and other raw materials. Many shipowners who received these ships were traditional customers of British yards and it is safe to say that more than a hundred orders were lost to British shipbuilders. Questions were raised in Parliament.

The 1938 naval programme was insignificant compared with the three previous years but the naval workloads in the yards concerned was keeping them very busy. So far as passenger liners were concerned, only a handful were delivered and these included two Union-Castle liners from Harland & Wolff, an Anchor Line vessel from Fairfield and a P&O vessel from Barclay, Curle. But a few yards were busy on liners ordered in previous years. John Brown were hard at work on the QUEEN ELIZABETH and Cammell Laird on the MAURETANIA for the same owners. Swan Hunter had in hand the DOMINION MONARCH for Shaw, Savill & Albion and Harland & Wolff was building the ANDES for Royal Mail Lines and PRETORIA CASTLE for Union-Castle. In this same year a week's summer holiday with pay was awarded to hourly-paid employees.

1939 opened with a number of yards still busy executing naval work but the pure merchant yards were rapidly running out of work as British owners continued to suffer from subsidised foreign competition. The shipping industry's repeated appeals to the Government for assistance finally paid off when finance was made available to subsidise cargo liner and tramp shipping, together with up to £10,000,000 in loans to encourage U.K. owners to place orders in U.K. yards. The Shipping Loan Bill never became law, overtaken by the outbreak of war which nullified the need for subsidies to shipowners. The Government however honoured the loans promised for new orders. Meanwhile the 1939 naval programme included orders for three cruisers of the "Mauritius" class —one with Swan Hunter, one with Vickers-Armstrongs at Barrow and one with John Brown.

In 1929, British shipbuilders were launching ton for ton with the rest of the world. In 1938, British shipbuilders were launching only in the region of one ton for every four or five launched abroad. The principal foreign competitors were Germany, Japan, the U.S.A. and Scandinavia.

During the nineteen year period under review, the industry had declined, not only in capacity but also in relation to the rest of the world's capacity, Table 1 illustrates the position.

TABLE 1

	U.K. Output 000s Gross Tons	% of World Output		U.K. Output 000s Gross Tons	% of World Output
1923	646	39.2	1931	502	31.1
1924	1,440	64.1	1932	188	25.8
1925	1,085	49.5	1933	133	27.2
1926	640	38.2	1934	460	47.5
1927	1,226	53.0	1935	499	38.3
1928	1.446	53.6	1936	856	40.4
1929	1,523	54.5	1937	921	34.2
1930	1,479	51.2	1938	1,030	34.0

1920—1939 REVIEW

Were the shipbuilders themselves wholly or partially to blame for this decline? The facts would not lead one to this conclusion.

In 1920, the industry's huge capacity was a carry-over from the First World War when this capacity was needed. The first shipbuilding depression of 1921-1926 and the second of 1930-1935 were not of the shipbuilders' making but the result of a slump in trade generally. In the whole of this nineteen year period, only 1920, 1927-1929 and 1936-1938 (a total of only seven years) were in any sense "fair to middling" for shipbuilders. In a total of twelve years of depression, only twice did the Government assist the industry. The first was in 1935 with a limited "scrap and build" scheme which ended a year later and the second in the Spring of 1939 and which had barely got underway when war was declared. The first scheme was in any case introduced when the market was already improving. As has been noted, it was the shipbuilders themselves who initiated and financed capacity reductions on a large scale over the eight year period commencing in 1930. Insofar as capacity and finance were concerned. therefore, the industry put its own house in order.

What of investment? For two reasons this was not significant. First, because most of the companies that made up the industry were all but bankrupt for long periods and this included even some of the largest companies. Second, because investment in plant and equipment was largely not needed (apart from the need to replace ageing plant). In any case ships had not changed to any great extent and neither had shipbuilding technology.

One feature of this period under review is significant. The yards that felt the pinch the most were those building basic cargo vessels and oil tankers. They did not refer to themselves as specialists but in fact that is what they were. The yards with experience of passenger liner and naval construction fared much better and they too built cargo ships, tankers etc. on occasion. The reason they fared better had little to do with efficiency but was simply the result of a reasonably steady market for the comparatively few builders of liners and the re-armament programme. So it appears with hindsight that a policy of product specialisation was questionable. The safer bet appeared to be to construct a wide variety of ship types for, by so doing, the chances were that at least one type would be in demand. This experience almost certainly led to many U.K. shipbuilders after the Second World War continuing to build a variety of ship types.

It is submitted therefore that the decline in U.K. shipbuilding between the Wars was not the fault of the industry but was merely the industry's reaction to two depressions in world trade. Nor did any contributory factor to this decline lie in the manner in which the industry was run.

CHAPTER 2

THE INDUSTRY AT WAR
1939—1945

When War was declared a proportion of the U.K. shipbuilding industry had benefited substantially from the four previous years of re-armament. These benefits did not, as has been shown, flow to the pure merchant shipyards, many of which had survived the two earlier slumps only by their fingertips. The Government's scheme to subsidise U.K. shipowners to order ships in U.K. yards had only been announced in the Spring of 1939 and while it prevented another slump in orders, it had not had time to mature before hostilities commenced. Thus it came about that while most of the large and medium-sized yards were busy with naval work, the rest of the industry was anything but fully employed. As has been stated earlier, in the course of the two trade slumps thousands of shipyard workers left the industry to seek employment elsewhere. Of those who remained a number were still unemployed.

The shipping industry had also suffered at the hands of two world trade depressions as well as from subsidised foreign competition. At the outbreak of the First World War in 1914, the U.K. shipping industry stood at 19.3 million tons and this total represented 39.3% of world shipping. In 1939, the U.K. shipping industry had declined to 17.9 million tons, but this total represented only 26.1% of world shipping because of the steady increase in the rest of the world's tonnage over the period.

In 1938 it was recognised that both the shipping and shipbuilding industries had declined to levels that were considered dangerous from the point of view of national defence and security. There were two reasons for arriving at this conclusion. First, experience in the First World War had amply demonstrated the losses to merchant shipping that could be inflicted by enemy submarines and Germany had been building a submarine fleet from 1935 onwards. Second, the U.S. Neutrality Act ensured that that country could not provide ships for a belligerent, nor could American ships sail into a war zone. It was therefore clear that in the event of war British shipbuilding had to be capable of rapid expansion in order to provide the means of sustaining the population with food and raw materials.

The Government had, in the previous year, requested the advice of the shipbuilding industry in an effort to formulate broad plans for maximising shipbuilding capacity in the event of war. In essence, the plan was simple— the industry would be assigned three main tasks viz. the building of naval ships, the building of standard merchant ships, and shiprepairing. Standard ships had been available from some of the merchant yards for two decades or more, but others, more up-to-date, had been developed by shipyard staffs during the two depressions, notably on the River Wear.

The Shipbuilding Employers Federation came into existence in 1899 for the purpose of dealing with wages, labour disputes and procedures on a national basis. Various shipbuilding river associations were in force prior to this date — the Wear Shipbuilders Association, for example, was founded as early as 1853. In more recent times, the Shipbuilding Conference had been formed, specifically to deal with the economic and commercial policy of the industry on a national basis. It was in fact the Conference who advised the Government on the shipbuilding strategy for wartime.

The Third Sea Lord, as Controller of the Navy, was responsible to the First Lord of the Admiralty for the construction and maintenance of naval ships. It was decided, six months after hostilities began, to appoint a second Controller who would rank on equal terms with the Third Sea Lord and who would be responsible to the First Lord of the Admiralty for the construction and maintenance of merchant shipping. Sir James Lithgow was duly appointed Controller of Merchant Shipbuilding and Repairs. Henceforth Sir James and his small staff controlled the allocation of merchant shipping work to each yard and was responsible for setting and monitoring shipbuilding programmes.

He and his staff were interested in any aspect of the shipbuilding process that impeded maximum production viz. material and manpower shortages, absenteeism, labour unrest, etc. It was clear that some authority had to be in place to ensure that the shipbuilding industry was given proper priority in the allocation of materials, notably steel. Many other industries were clamouring for steel such as the manufacturers of tanks. Not least among those clamouring for steel was the Controller of the Navy!

Early in the war, the Essential Works Order was introduced to provide a form of civil mobilisation. On paper, it enabled employers to direct labour to any point where it was needed, from yard to yard and from district to district. In addition, employees on scheduled work could not leave it without official permission. Absenteeism was punishable, but employees could not be sacked without the same official permission. Not surprisingly, the Order was difficult to operate.

It proved timely to set up the Controller of Merchant Shipbuilding and Repairs and his staff at an early point in the war, since right from the outset problems arose of very great magnitude. Enemy submarines began to sink an ever-increasing number of Allied vessels in the Atlantic and elsewhere and as a result, the demands for merchant vessels were hugely accelerated. At home, there was an acute shortage of shipbuilding workers, despite the numbers unemployed before 3rd September 1939.

The fact was that they were brought back into the industry but were largely employed on naval work. The repair yards, too, were facing a huge programme of conversion work—modifying passenger ships into troopships and armed merchant cruisers and all manner of other conversion work, not to mention an ever increasing number of damage repairs. The repairers were also engaged in the task of arming merchant vessels with anti-aircraft guns and equipping them with gear for mine avoidance.

The shipyards themselves were required to undertake civil defence such as air-raid precautions, fire watching and first-aid. Arrangements had to be made for the "blackout" of all premises. Staff and hourly-paid employees found much of their free time taken up by Home Guard and Civil Defence duties.

So far as orders were concerned, from day one of the war all ship ordering came under state control, in line with the recommendations made by the Shipbuilding Conference in 1937. Henceforth, the Admiralty, in consultation with the Conference, ordered all new vessels. They also ordered all merchant vessels required by the Ministry of Supply. A few vessels were allocated to shipping lines, but these had to be licensed by the Admiralty and licences were normally only granted for vessels replacing those sunk by enemy action.

Orders for standard ships were placed by the Admiralty with many yards and while machinery and equipment were fully standardised, the hulls were of standard types but of varying sizes. The ships were allocated such that each was the biggest that the particular yard could build quickly and economically. Standard tankers, both sea-going and coastal, were also ordered with a number of shipbuilders. The war at sea was going to be fought with oil-fired and diesel-engined ships— hence the imperative requirement for tankers.

Welding began to be adopted in shipbuilding prior to the outbreak of war, but riveting remained the principal means of joining together a ship's structure. In this respect, the construction of standard ships complied with the experience, facilities and trained labour within the industry. Not so with naval vessels, where a higher proportion of welding was specified. Those yards engaged in warship work had therefore not only to install the necessary cabling and equipment, but also train operatives. This was difficult for two reasons. First, because of the reluctance of skilled men to be retrained in welding skills. This problem was overcome, with the agreement of the unions, by training "dilutees"—that is, men who were not time-served boilermakers. Second, because of the disruption caused to their huge workload by the installation of the electric cabling.

The advantages of welding versus riveting were already appreciated by shipbuilders in the late 'thirties. There was an obvious saving in steel weight, because of the elimination of plate overlaps and to a lesser extent, the further weight saving achieved by the elimination of rivets. The steel weight saving, of course, reduced the first cost of the vessel but more importantly resulted in a corresponding increase in deadweight of the vessel and thus benefited the shipowner during the life of that vessel. But there were a number of imponderables concerning electric welding. First, was a welded structure likely to be too rigid in varying sea states and if so, would cracking result? Riveting by comparison, allowed the structure to flex at sea. Second, would hull construction not prove more difficult in practice? With plate edge meeting plate edge, much more accuracy would be mandatory. Riveting, again by

A heavily-censored photograph of H.M.S. PRINCE OF WALES — a battleship of 35,000 tons standard displacement completed by Cammell Laird & Co. Ltd. in 1941. W.S.P.L.

EMPIRE LANCER — a standard cargo vessel of 7,037 gross tons built by Lithgows Ltd. in 1942.   *W.S.P.L.*

comparison, provided not only a margin for error because of the plate overlaps, but also provided the means of connecting one plate to another during the process of erection. Third, would plating deform during the welding process? All of these questions could only be answered by trial and error and U.K. shipbuilders were in any case in no position to commit themselves to capital expenditure in the late 'thirties. Capital expenditure, of course, was necessary to equip each yard with the welding equipment required, which for a start meant laying power cables in ducts for each building berth and for the steel sheds. During the course of the war, welding was gradually introduced and ships' structures were modified accordingly.

In merchant ships, the first structural change was made by eliminating plate butt overlaps, while retaining riveted seams. This change was to prove fundamental to the later development of ship construction generally. Up to this point, ship Classification Societies required that the layout of shell plating incorporated what was referred to as a "shift of butts". That is to say, the butts of shell plating were required to be staggered for reasons of strength continuity. Henceforth plate butts were arranged in line, thus permitting a rectangular panel of stiffened plating to be produced. This in turn encouraged the prefabrication of shell panels, deck panels, etc. that heralded entirely new concepts of ship construction and shipyard layout. These had to wait until the war ended and for a little time thereafter.

The war continued and by the end of 1941 the U.S.A. was planning to provide 1.5 million tons of shipping to carry Lend-Lease cargoes. It also planned to produce no less than 7 million tons of new shipping from U.S. yards in 1942. The main products of these arrangements were the so-called "Liberty" cargo ship and the "T.2" tanker. The former was evolved from a design of standard cargo ship developed during the second depression by J. L. Thompson of Sunderland.

Meanwhile U.K. ship losses were rising alarmingly throughout 1942 when a total of 1,000 U.K. controlled vessels were sunk. The shipbuilding industry, working flat out though it was, was unable to keep pace with the losses and the size of the U.K. controlled merchant fleet began to decline. Some yards had suffered grievously from air-raids which badly disrupted production. John Brown's yard for example, was twice bombed during the first half of 1941, although the town of Clydebank and not the yard itself sustained most damage. A devastating air-raid engulfed Harland & Wolff's Belfast yard in May of the same year and two-thirds of their entire premises were destroyed. J. L. Thompson of Sunderland was attacked two years later.

Later in 1942, U.K. yards were stepping up production of standard ships and by 1943 the tide was turning as more Allied ships were produced and at the same time the U-Boat menace began to recede. At the same time, though, shipyard labour remained in short supply and the demands made of the yards were met by employing female labour extensively on a wide variety of duties. They were trained in burning, welding, painting and other skills as well as undertaking cleaning duties.

The aircraft carrier H.M.S. INDEFATIGABLE of 26,000 tons standard displacement completed by John Brown & Co. Ltd. in 1944.   W.S.P.L.

Loch class frigate H.M.S. LOCH TRALAIG built by the Caledon Shipbuilding & Engineering Co. Ltd. in 1944.   Builders' photograph

The unremitting pressure on the yards continued right up to the end of the war in 1945. By that time, 60% of the pre-war U.K. fleet— some 11.3 million tons —had been lost. This loss was largely made up, after the war, by wartime U.K. built ships, purchases from the U.S.A., enemy prize tonnage and ships allocated to the U.K. by the Inter-Allied Reparations Agency. As a result, between 1939 and 1946, the decline of the U.K fleet was restricted to 3.6 million tons or 21%.

Other countries fared considerably worse than the U.K. insofar as percentage fleet losses were concerned. The following indicates the position:

COUNTRY	% LOSS
Italy	91
Germany	90
Japan	78
Greece	70
France	56
Holland	44
Belgium	43
Norway	40
U.K.	21 (after reparations)

In total, 32 million tons of shipping was lost in the Second World War.

The efforts of U.K. shipbuilders were crucial to ultimate victory, particularly in the earlier years of the war, after the fall of France and before the U.S.A. entered the fray. The tonnage outputs from the various shipbuilding centres was truly impressive in every year of the conflict and reached its peak in 1943. Though there was little time for investment, the yards did in fact try to effect improvements in facilities and welding was rivalling riveting as the means of joining steel together.

CHAPTER 3

YEARS OF CHANGE
1946—1960

For the first few years after hostilities ceased, U.K. shipbuilders were kept extremely busy replacing war-time losses sustained by U.K. shipowners who, as has been noted, suffered nowhere nearly as badly as their competitors. The replacement programme was, however, large enough to keep U.K. yards fully occupied for a number of years. U.K. shipbuilders did contract ships for foreign account but these represented a modest proportion of their output. Most shipbuilders continued to build a wide variety of products and the products themselves were largely similar in size and type to the ships they replaced. In short, the U.K. shipbuilder saw no need for radical changes in design, construction, facilities or order books.

Soon after the war ended, U.K. shipowners operated 27% of world tonnage and their traditional links with U.K. yards had been re-established. Over the same period, U.K. shipbuilders represented some 51% of world output. The future for both looked good.

Not surprisingly, warship construction reduced to a trickle. The traditional builders of the larger warships, some of whom had been very busy since hostilities ended converting armed merchant cruisers and troopships back into passenger liners, began to receive orders for new passenger ships. Many of these orders revived pre-war links between owner and builder, P&O and Orient Line with Vickers-Armstrongs, Union-Castle and Royal Mail with Harland & Wolff, Cunard with John Brown, Canadian Pacific with Fairfield, etc. ·

CHANGES FACED BY SHIPOWNERS

Profound changes however were soon to take place affecting both U.K. shipowners and foreign shipbuilders. The changes to shipowners affected all three main sections — liner trades, tramps and tankers.

LINERS

Whereas pre-1939, U.K. liner owners enjoyed a dominant position on many routes, the world political map was being re-drawn in the years immediately post-war. The granting of independence to India in 1947 and to Burma in the following year together with the establishment of the People's Republic of China the year after, severely restricted U.K. liner owners' long-standing services to these regions.

In the New World, equally profound changes were occurring which seriously reduced the scale of U.K. liner services. The U.S. Government announced that of the massive tonnages of cargo transported from the U.S.A. to Europe representing Marshall Aid one half was to be loaded in U.S. owned ships.

CITY OF JOHANNESBURG — a cargo/passenger ship of 8,207 gross tons built for Ellerman Lines Ltd. by Barclay, Curle & Co. Ltd. in 1947. W.S.P.L.

The Caledon Shipyard at Dundee embodied a layout typical of the period. The first phase of modernisation can be seen with a prefabrication shed built on No. 5 Berth. circa 1951. Author's collection

Other countries, like Brazil for example, adopted similar practices in relation to imports and exports.

In addition to being deprived of a great number of trade routes, U.K. liner owners found themselves facing subsidised competition from the U.S.A., from a number of Communist countries and even from western Europe. Further bad news came in the form of United States and West German funds being made available to West German owners for reconstruction of their fleets. Finally, the "flag of convenience" vessel developed into a major force.

TRAMPS

U.K. tramp owners, although not so seriously affected by the foregoing changes as U.K. liner owners, deferred placing orders in U.K. yards in the belief that a shipping slump would shortly take place, similar to that which occurred a few years after World War I. Following such a slump, they believed, they could negotiate bargain prices in U.K. yards. Far from a slump occurring, world trade was expanding rapidly and with it seaborne trade. Freight rates climbed and were to escalate in the ten years following, given the impetus of the Korean War in 1950/52 and the first closure of the Suez Canal in 1956/57.

Thus the U.K. tramp fleet declined while those of its competitors, and some of these were newcomers to shipping, expanded. By 1955, the era of the bulk carrier had arrived but this significant milestone in seaborne transport was at this point largely ignored by U.K. tramp owners.

OIL TANKERS

The third main section of merchant shipping—namely the owners of oil-tankers — were undergoing the biggest change of all. Carriage of oil by sea had hugely expanded and by ten years or so after the end of the war had increased by 400% compared to 1939. Over the same period the U.K. tanker fleet increased only modestly. Whereas pre-war. the bulk of the world's tanker fleet, U.K. included, was owned and operated by oil companies, in the early 50s Norwegian and Greek owners, relative newcomers to tanker owning, entered the field in a big way.

After the debacle in 1951, when the Persian Government nationalised the local Anglo-Iranian Oil Company's facilities, the U.K., Holland, Germany and other large importers of oil were prompted to construct their own oil refineries. The carriage of oil thereafter was largely limited to crude oil from Middle East and other oil fields. Soon the size of oil tankers began to grow rapidly as the economies of scale began to be realised.

The rapidly increasing size of the seaborne oil trade was nothing short of a boom and this continued virtually without interruption until 1973. But like U.K. tramp owners, U.K. tanker owners were but modestly involved.

By a twist of irony, the newcomers to the ranks of tanker owners were offered attractive credit facilities in the U.K. and these arrangements allowed the vessels concerned to be re-registered under flags of convenience immediately after the loans had been repaid within the seven year repayment period. Under boom conditions, these arrangements were highly profitable for the owners concerned—for two reasons. First, the capital costs of the vessels were spread over seven years while in many cases the profits earned on a few voyages were enough to cover this. Second, the operating costs after seven years were drastically reduced because of the tax benefits and low crew costs synonymous with flags of convenience.

The result of these fundamental changes in world trade, discrimination, size and types of vessel was to increase the world's dry cargo fleet over the ten years up to 1960 by 50%. Over the same period, the world's tanker fleet grew by no less than 225%. Over roughly the same period the U.K. fleet as a percentage of the world fleet fell by 4%.

PASSENGER LINERS

Travel by sea reached its peak in 1957 and was then to be all but eliminated by the jet airliner. By the mid-60s, the cruise business began to expand.

In 1957 also, the first ro-ro ship made its appearance.

FOREIGN SHIPYARD CHANGES

These then were the changes forced upon the U.K. builder's traditional and best customer, the U.K. shipowner. Changes were also rapidly taking place within the U.K. shipbuilder's competitors, notably in West Germany and Japan. The heavily damaged shipyards in these countries were granted U.S. funds for reconstruction and in a very short time were building ships with the most up-to-date plant and machinery.

Sweden, which had remained neutral throughout the war, had developed welding and prefabrication techniques. After the war they had the money and the techniques to modernise as well as having the 'green field' sites to lay out new yards.

U.K. yards at the end of the war had neither the money for modernisation nor the availability of 'green field' sites but were, as already stated, content at the prospect of replacing U.K. owners' wartime losses using their existing equipment. By the early 50s West German and Japanese shipbuilders were increasing their output rapidly, while Swedish shipbuilders led world shipbuilding output. In fact, although U.K. shipbuilding output increased by 12.5% between 1948 and 1960 its percentage of world output fell from 51% to 16%. Very significantly, the percentage of tonnage delivered by U.K. yards to U.K. owners over the same period fell from 100% to 80%.

DECLINE OF U.K.—RISE OF JAPAN

Thus, despite seaborne world trade having doubled between 1948 and 1960, U.K. shipowners and shipbuilders were both in relative decline, especially the latter. By 1960 too, Japan had become the world's largest shipbuilder. But unlike U.K. shipowners, who had received Government compensation for war losses and had since the war ended built up reserves on the back of a buoyant shipping market, U.K. shipbuilders only began making good profits from 1947 onwards, after enduring fourteen years of depression between the wars which depleted their reserves.

This then was the manner in which world shipping expanded over the fourteen years following the end of World War II. This same period witnessed the relative decline of U.K. shipowners as a percentage of world tonnage. It was against this background that the U.K. shipbuilder operated. The reasons for the steady increase in world shipping have already been stated. Why was it not possible for the U.K. shipbuilding industry to expand during this prosperous period? There were a number of reasons.

REASONS

First, the trauma of not one but two shipbuilding depressions in the eighteen years prior to the outbreak of World War II was an experience not likely to be forgotten by those shipbuilders whose businesses survived those terrible times. Many of them had not enjoyed full order books in the whole of this period and so caution dictated that increasing capacity in the late 40s might only serve to hasten the return of empty berths.

Second, the question of economics. For the first time in eighteen years, pure merchant shipbuilders were making good profits. Only now were the shareholders being rewarded for their patience and to deny them a return now on their investment in favour of capital improvements seemed at the time to be both ungrateful and premature. Of course reserves started to be made in the accounts which, it was intended, would, in due time, be used to finance schemes of modernisation.

Third, the question of industrial relations. The man hours lost through strikes, demarcation disputes, overtime bans, etc. began to increase, slowly at first, until by 1960 they had reached serious proportions. In the late 50s, yards had begun to modernise, but just when it seemed that the U.K. could begin to compete with the Swedes, the West Germans and the emerging Japanese, wholly unrealistic demands were made by labour both for manning levels and for wages in relation to the operation of the new and costly machinery. The change from "piece-part" riveted shipbuilding to prefabricated welded shipbuilding involved a much deeper change.

The industry was henceforth not so much craft-intensive as capital-intensive. Hitherto, highly skilled craftsmen operating mainly on a system of piecework or its equivalent and supervised by hard and knowledgeable foremen produced quality ships from pretty basic plant and equipment. Such craftsmen and their semi-skilled and unskilled helpers had known dole-queues before the war and were now very content to find themselves in continuous employment. But things were beginning to change—for the worse. The spur given to production by the threat of unemployment had waned as a result of the heavy workload. Apprentice tradesmen engaged after the war ended had never known the dole. Thus it came about that by the late 50s, the industry was bedevilled with labour problems.

Despite the increasing incidence of labour problems, U.K. shipbuilders, with the benefit of a secure albeit shrinking home market and with the benefit of a buoyant dry cargo and tanker market, not to mention passenger ships, were able to make good profits over this period. The reason they were able to do this was by a continuous increase in shipbuilding prices. Output displayed a remarkable consistency, as can be seen from the table below:

Year	Output (000s Gross tons)	YEAR	Output (000s Gross tons)
1948	1,176	1955	1,474
1949	1,267	1956	1,383
1950	1,325	1957	1,414
1951	1,341	1958	1,402
1952	1,303	1959	1,373
1953	1,317	1960	1,331
1954	1,409		

The real decline of the industry started in the 60s and thereafter accelerated in the 70s and 80s.

*The turbine-driven cargo liner THESEUS of 7,800 gross tons built for Alfred Holt &
Co. by the Caledon Shipbuilding & Engineering Co. Ltd. in 1955.   Author's collection*

*The Replenishment Tanker PEARLEAF built for the Royal Fleet Auxiliary by the
Blythswood Shipbuilding Co. Ltd. in 1960.   Michael Lennon*

CHAPTER 4

CLOSURES AND RE-ORGANISATION 1960—1968

THE SHIPPING MARKET

We have already seen how world events—the increase in air traffic, the economies of scale in the operations of large tankers and bulk carriers, the development of the ro-ro ship and (later) the container ship, transformed the operations of shipowners. U.K. shipowners adapted, albeit somewhat late, to these changes. U.K. shipbuilders made attempts to adapt to the changes necessary to construct the new types of vessels and at the same time, match more and more competition, not only from West Germany and Japan, but later from a host of other nations who began to build their own vessels—Yugoslavia, Brazil, Korea and China to mention but four. A number of these benefited from Government subsidies.

In the late 50s the process of adaptation was hastened by first, a temporary but severe fall in world demand for ships and second, by the growing might of the competition—notably Japan and West Germany, both of whom had recently exceeded U.K. output. A number of U.K. yards used this order famine to modernise their facilities.

Not all sections of the shipping market were depressed however, and this applied particularly to the tanker market. Sizes of tankers had increased dramatically and were around 65,000 tons deadweight maximum at this time. Only the largest yards were in a position to construct these and these yards included all the builders of passenger liners. The sizes of bulk carriers had also increased and around this period orders were placed for vessels of this type up to 50,000 tons deadweight. Only those yards with berths capable of being greatly extended could tackle ships of this size and such firms included Furness Shipbuilding at Haverton Hill and J. L. Thompson and Sir James Laing of Sunderland.

In 1960, the Shipbuilding Industry's Central Organisations set up an extensive review of shipbuilding methods both in the U.K. and abroad. The Patton Committee, consisting of shipbuilders drawn from a number of U.K. yards, produced a Report published in 1962. The Report outlined the improvements necessary in methods of production in U.K. yards.

INDIVIDUAL SHIPYARD RESPONSES TO THE SHIPPING MARKET

Yards which were not in a position to construct these large vessels suffered mixed fortunes, whether modernised or not. On the River Clyde, for example, Barclay, Curle survived probably because of its invaluable connections with a number of U.K. liner companies (although it was to close down in 1967). Similar considerations applied to Connells, specifically in their association with Ben Line of Edinburgh. Greenock Dockyard, owned by the Clan Line, continued to build a succession of vessels for their owner. Scotts' had modernised and were now able to construct tankers and bulkers of up to 40,000 tons deadweight.

Blythswood, Harland & Wolff at Govan, William Hamilton and Denny all closed—the first named because although a tanker specialist, it was restricted in the size of such vessels it could build. The other three closed for the same reason or because of the impending demise of the cargo liner.

On the North East coast it was the same story with the closures of William Gray's yards at Hartlepool, Short Brothers at Sunderland and Blyth Shipbuilding at Blyth. The survival of Readheads on the Tyne, Bartrams and Doxfords on the Wear and Smith's Dock on the Tees were for different reasons. Readheads had excellent connections with a number of U.K. owners, especially Strick Line. Bartrams and Doxfords were noted tramp builders of great efficiency and survived these times with the construction of such vessels. Smith's Dock was also a highly efficient yard and survived on a diet of tramps and modest sized tankers.

While the bulk of the shipping market remained depressed some yards turned to alternative sources of work in order to keep going. During this period for example, John Brown built five jack-up drilling rigs for Texan owners while Harland & Wolff built an exploration drill rig for B.P. Both companies were faced with many technical problems in constructing these rigs. Harland & Wolff in particular registered a notable success by launching its rig complete —each of the three legs sliding on launchways positioned on three adjacent building berths! The Caledon yard at Dundee contracted to fabricate the massive girders for the Tay Road Bridge and in so doing lost a great deal of money.

Around this time, Vickers-Armstrongs at Barrow and Cammell Laird were in the process of modifications to berths, buildings and equipment in readiness for the construction of Polaris submarines. Both these yards had, in addition, recently completed huge modernisation programmes and were now equipped to build a wide range of ship types including large passenger liners, tankers in excess of 100,000 tons deadweight and a wide range of naval ships. In addition, Cammell Laird had developed a series of standard cargo ships, bulk carriers and tankers.

Vickers-Armstrongs' Naval Yard on Tyneside contracted to build five highly sophisticated cargo liners for their good customer Alfred Holt of Liverpool. Eight ships in all were ordered—two with Mitsubishi and one with John Brown made up the total. They were known as the "Glenalmond" class. Despite their experience in building for this owner, Vickers-Armstrongs were grievously late in delivery and incurred severe losses. From this point on, Alfred Holt only ordered two further ships in the U.K.—the rest were built in Japan.

The Furness Shipbuilding Company on the Tees, owned since 1951 by Sears Holdings, ran out of work in 1963. In 1965 a number of orders for large bulk carriers were secured and in order to construct these, the berths and craneage were increased and new fabrication facilities provided. The yard was now capable of constructing ships up to 170,000 tons deadweight and ships of this size were constructed in later years.

OPALIA of 32,122 gross tons built for Shell Tankers Ltd. by Cammell Laird & Co. Ltd. in 1963.   *W.S.P.L.*

The Jack-Up Drilling Rig GULFTIDE built for the Offshore Drilling Co. by John Brown & Co. (Clydebank) Ltd. in 1967.   *Builders' photograph*

43

Some yards undertook marketing and employed agents abroad for this purpose. Others like John Brown did very little, the result almost certainly of their heavy reliance on four valued U.K. customers—Cunard, New Zealand Shipping Company, B.P. and the Royal Navy. Nor did John Brown offer any standard ships, but relied on an owner's design being developed jointly by owner and builder.

Harland & Wolff on the other hand built for a wide range of owners, mainly but not exclusively, in the U.K. So too did Swan Hunter and to a lesser extent Cammell Laird and Fairfield. Vickers-Armstrongs came to rely more and more on naval work, especially submarines and in the mid 60s ceased altogether the construction of merchant ships.

In a parallel with the years between the wars, the large yards fared best, sharing orders for naval vessels both surface and subsea and also for the odd passenger liner. Harland & Wolff, Vickers-Armstrongs and Cammell Laird each built their last passenger liner in this period—CANBERRA, ORIANA and WINDSOR CASTLE respectively. John Brown built the TRANSVAAL CASTLE at the same time and continued to build such vessels in subsequent years with tragic losses.

The surviving medium-sized and smaller yards, builders of tramps and tankers pre-war and now cargo vessels, bulk carriers and tankers, faced massive competition from well-equipped foreign yards while traditional U.K. tramp and tanker owners appeared content to see their relative decline in seaborne transportation continue. These same U.K. owners had been among the yards' best customers, although as Hilditch has correctly stated "The greatest range of customers could be found amongst the builders of cargo tramps". These yards had also modernised although not on the scale of the big composite yards—such schemes would have been entirely beyond their means to finance. A number of these businesses were family-owned and this fact has led some to suggest that this was a further reason for the industry's decline. It is submitted that some family-owned yards were better than others just as some publicly-owned yards were better than others. There can be no doubting that the cargo tramp builders had to market harder and sharpen their pencils finer than the big composite yards, fed as they were on a diet of cost-plus naval and passenger ships. And as we shall see, these were the very yards which were to register such huge losses and had, each in their own way, to be bailed out.

Virtually all U.K. shipyards had been severely constrained in their modernisation schemes by the hemmed-in nature of their premises. Most U.K. yards by the mid 60s had modernised to some degree or another, but it is highly questionable if due consideration was given to what the future types of product would be. The size and shape of potential orders should determine to a large extent the scope of modernisation plans. But as we have already seen, it was not only the nature and expanding size of seaborne trade that was changing, it was also the shipowners themselves.

The U.K. passenger and cargo liner trades had for many years been dominated by a few powerful shipping companies, all of whom had established

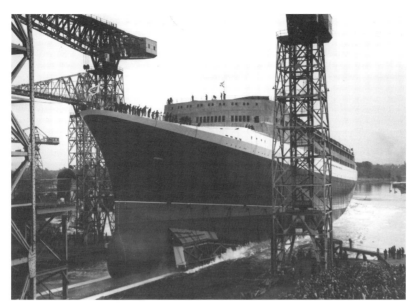

The launch of QUEEN ELIZABETH 2 on 20th September 1967 from the yard of John Brown & Co. (Clydebank) Ltd. *Builders' photograph*

One of the last cargo liners — the M.V. GLENFINLAS of 12,094 gross tons built for Glen Line Ltd. by John Brown & Co. (Clydebank) Ltd. in 1967. *Builders' photograph*

connections with specific U.K. yards. Tanker trades however, were no longer dominated by a few powerful oil companies, some of whom also had established connections with U.K. yards. Clearly these arrangements were coming to an end. U.K. tramp owners were giving way to foreign based owners of bulk carriers.

With hindsight it is relatively easy to point out the foregoing changes and the impact that they ought to have had on U.K. shipbuilders' strategy for the future. In most cases, the yards were modernised within their existing boundaries, berths and craneage and equipment were installed to enable them to build the biggest ship that was practicable.

Much criticism has been levelled at shipbuilding managements for their failure to formulate a product strategy at this time. It is further alleged that since the capital-intensive nature of the new yard layouts were conducive to mass production of standard ships, management was doubly guilty of failure to realise the potential throughput expansion at hand. It has already been noted how, in the years before the Second World War, those yards with experience of building warships and passenger ships fared much better than the pure merchant yards. The experience immediately post-war did little to change this belief in the merits of product variety.

There was in any case scope for product variety. It was not as if the significant reduction in passenger liner, warship and tramp ship ordering had not been replaced by other types of vessels. There was however an ingrained reluctance to "place all their eggs in one basket", and it seemed perfectly valid to construct tankers, bulk carriers and ro-ros in the same yard, with reasonable production runs of each type on the basis of multiple orders. Two yards were notable exceptions and while both of them were success stories, there were special reasons for this, as will be explained later. The yards in question were Austin & Pickersgill and Appledore Shipbuilders.

By the mid 60s, most U.K. yards had spent varying sums of money on modernisation. Those whose plans had been more modest were able to submit lower prices for the little business available than those whose plans had been more grandiose. This turn of events only demonstrated that the one certain result of upgrading facilities was an increase in fixed overheads.

The closures of the early 60s already noted only helped to strengthen the view of the Conservative Government that the industry had to contract, but the Government were of course assuming that it would be the medium and smaller yards that would take, once more, the brunt of the contraction. The Government noted that new orders booked were only equivalent to 40% of a reduced output. Moreover, employment in the industry had fallen significantly. In view of this, a credit scheme was introduced in 1963 for the purpose of financing U.K. owners to place orders in U.K. yards. The scheme was set to last for only twelve months and initially £30 million was made available, later doubled to £60 million, in view of the immediate response to the scheme. A large amount of tonnage was contracted as a result and in order to accommodate credit for the "Q.E.2" the limit was raised still further.

In 1964 a Labour Government was elected and shortly afterwards set up a committee of enquiry under Reay Geddes to recommend the steps necessary to place the industry on an internationally competitive basis. The Geddes Report was published in February 1966 and in essence proposed:-

1) The establishment of a Shipbuilding Industry Board (S.I.B.), which would, among other things, administer and control Government financial assistance.

2) The availability of Government loans "aimed at facilitating desirable groupings and accelerating the rationalisation of resources" and

3) The availability of grants for transitional losses.

Following the end of the home owners credit scheme in 1964, U.K. orders to U.K. yards fell dramatically. At this point the Board of Trade helped to promote export business by improved export credit terms.

In the autumn of 1965 came the sudden announcement of the closure of Fairfield's large yard at Govan. After much lobbying by M.P.s, town councillors, trade union officials and shop stewards and later by the personal appearance of Mr. George Brown M.P., a group of Glasgow businessmen was persuaded to purchase the yard. In this they were assisted by Government finance and to a lesser extent, by trade union finance. One of the businessmen concerned—Mr. Iain Stewart (later Sir Iain)—became Chairman.

He was determined to prove that the extensive use of modern planning techniques could be applied to the shipbuilding process. He also strongly felt that a more open relationship should be developed between management and labour. Thus began early in 1966 the so-called "Fairfield Experiment".

Fairfields (Glasgow) Ltd., remained in being for just two years before being absorbed into Upper Clyde Shipbuilders in February 1968. Whether the company would have prospered on its own has been the subject of much controversy. Certainly wage rates shot up, but whether this was in response to genuine increases in productivity has never actually been proved. Accusations were made by others at the time that productivity bonuses were being paid in advance of their achievement.

Large numbers of planning staff were recruited for the purpose of initiating and operating work study, value analysis and productivity schemes. The top management were scathing in their comments about the methods adopted by other yards and especially about their attitude to trade unions in general. But whatever the truth was about the level of productivity achieved, the wage levels prevailing at Fairfields (Glasgow) Ltd. in 1968 were anything but helpful to Upper Clyde Shipbuilders when it took over wage negotiations across its five yards.

The finance made available by Government to Fairfields (Glasgow) Ltd., marked the start of its intervention in shipbuilding. This was followed by the formation of the Shipbuilding Industry Board, a body conceived by the Geddes Report of 1966.

From the onset of mergers in 1968, the S.I.B. approved grants and loans only to those firms which amalgamated (with the exception of Harland & Wolff, Cammell Laird, Appledore and the three companies on the River Wear, all of which remained separate).

47

CHAPTER 5

GOVERNMENTS GET INVOLVED
1968—1972

UPPER CLYDE SHIPBUILDERS LTD.

The fact that the Ministry of Technology, the S.I.B. and an S.I.B. working party all originally favoured a single group for the Clyde may be evidence of shipbuilders being the best judges of what was best for the industry. It was a very good thing that such a scheme never materialised, not just because the later U.C.S. collapse could well have brought down the Lower Clyde as well, but on the immediate impact such a merger would have had on Lower Clyde wage rates and therefore costs.

In the event, the five shipyards—John Brown, Charles Connell, Fairfields (Glasgow), Alexander Stephen and Yarrow agreed to merge in line with the S.I.B. working party's recommendations. Their report proposed in addition that Connell and Stephen be phased out with an overall reduction in labour of 5,500.

What persuaded the working party to propose the phasing out of Connell in particular remains a mystery. It was the only one of the five yards with any hope of building merchant ships, notably bulk carriers, within range of international prices.

The yards concerned placed conditions on their offer to merge:
1) It was subject to financial assistance from the S.I.B.
2) Yarrow was to remain an independent subsidiary retaining its name and board.
3) It was subject to the signing of an employment charter and
4) It was subject to the approval of all shareholders.
Numerous accounts of the short life of U.C.S. have been published and it may be appropriate therefore not to reiterate the financial crises blow by blow, but rather deal with the fundamental causes of the collapse.

For a start, U.C.S. inherited a poor order book, with the exception of Yarrow. This was not justified by the state of the dry cargo market which had improved and still less by the booming tanker market. Clearly this state of affairs could not be laid at the door of U.C.S.

Only two of the executive directors of the U.C.S. board had any shipbuilding experience — the technical and financial directors of John Brown. The Chairman and Chief Executive and the three other executive board members were all new to shipbuilding and they made clear their view that a shipyard was just like any other factory or business where standard business principles

48

applied. In this they may have been correct but it was clear that they were not prepared for the Confederation of Shipbuilding and Engineering Unions!

It would be difficult to imagine a more ill-matched collection of shipbuilding companies. John Brown, tradition bursting at the seams, was outfitting the QUEEN ELIZABETH 2 (employing 80% of its workforce) and had little other work. Fairfields (Glasgow), eschewed by the other four, was cocky about its alleged productivity gains. Yarrow was now continuing operations with a certain detachment. Stephen was running short of work. Connell was run on a shoe-string.

Personalities abounded in shipbuilding and the five yards concerned had their share. Add to this the fierce pride each yard's management took in its own yard and future welfare and one has a situation requiring a strong and sure touch when overseeing such a group.

Apart from the order shortage, one other factor dogged U.C.S. from start-up. Again it was not their fault. It concerned the fact that much of the initial finance made available by the S.I.B. had to be used to reimburse the shareholders, thus imposing a shortage of working capital upon the group. That said, what followed from then on certainly was solely the fault of U.C.S.

The unions flatly refused to discuss, let alone implement, the proposed 5,500 reduction in the labour force. Instead of attempting to reopen discussions or calling for volunteers for redundancy or trying to reduce overtime working, U.C.S. promptly offered a guarantee of employment for 2 years—for all 13,000 employees! Danny McGarvey, General Secretary of the Boilermakers led the union delegation throughout the early part of the U.C.S. saga and knew how to exploit a change in circumstances. This first taste of blood by the unions was to augur badly for the future. In view of this commitment to labour, U.C.S. had to find work fast. This it proceeded to do by slashing prices.

Meanwhile Fairfields (Glasgow) had, immediately prior to vesting, committed itself to wage increases. U.C.S. could not risk a strike because of the lack of working capital and so conceded the increase across the other four yards.

U.C.S. set up their H.Q. at Fitzpatrick House in the centre of Glasgow. This was an expensive new office block and was soon being filled by large numbers of staff. This staff was all in addition to the existing staffs in the five yards and as such, represented a considerable additional overhead burden.

The shortage of working capital, the low-priced contracts and the increased overheads soon resulted in the first of many financial crises for the company. This occurred in February 1969 and was followed by others in June and August 1969. Between February and August U.C.S. received no less than £19.3 million, although they had requested more. What is amazing about all this is how the "penny did not drop" with Government until 1971.

The "new brooms" brought in to improve labour relations and productivity met with little or no success. The outfitting of QUEEN ELIZABETH 2 for example provided fertile ground for wage demands from the outfit trades, while the

The Polaris submarine H.M.S. REPULSE completed by Vickers-Armstrongs (Shipbuilders) Ltd. in 1968.   W.S.P.L.

The 37,850 tons deadweight bulk carrier M.V. VOLNAY on sea-trials in 1969. Built by Upper Clyde Shipbuilders (Clydebank Division) for Harrisons (Clyde) Ltd.
Builders' photograph

widely differing yard wage rates and systems of payment between similar trades in the boilermakers were also exploited. Mobility of labour was another problem area. The multiplicity of unresolved labour problems led to delayed deliveries and cost overruns on contracts already taken at rock-bottom prices.

The delays in production caused instalment payments to be delayed by the shipowners. U.C.S. proceeded to delay payments to sub-contractors for goods already delivered. Sub-contractors retaliated by withholding supplies which further delayed the subject vessels.

The QUEEN ELIZABETH 2 delivery debacle was something U.C.S. could have done without. It has to be said at this point that the contract delivery date of end-November 1968 was always going to be difficult to meet.

Obsessed by the desire to abandon traditional shipbuilding practices, U.C.S. decided that it wanted no truck with the established procedure for the resolution of labour disputes. In particular, it ignored the existence of the long-established Clyde Shipbuilders' Association with its small team of highly efficient and experienced negotiators. It proposed in fact to develop its own negotiating procedures. This was a crucial error on the part of U.C.S. for instead of union delegations facing up to a set of hard-nosed realists they were met by a set of well-intentioned newcomers to the realms of labour relations brinkmanship.

Another feature of U.C.S. operations that contributed to its financial downfall was the extent to which management consultants were utilised — five different consultants were at work at Clydebank simultaneously and they don't come cheap! Nor do they assist production management in keeping its "eye on the ball".

U.C.S. finally collapsed in June 1971 with a net deficiency of £20 million after the Government (now Tory) refused further aid.

SCOTT LITHGOW LTD.

In 1967, in response to the Geddes recommendations, Scotts', Lithgows, Ferguson Brothers and Scott & Sons of Bowling put to the S.I.B. their proposal to merge. These included plans for extending Lithgows' facilities, for which financial assistance was required. The scheme was duly approved and Scott Lithgow Ltd came into being in 1969.

In some ways it was a curious marriage. Scotts', founded in 1711, was believed to be the world's oldest shipbuilder. By 1969 it was a medium-sized shipyard with its own engine works. It counted among its customers some highly prestigious names—the Royal Navy, the Royal Fleet Auxiliary, Alfred Holt, Elder Dempster and many others. It was one of only three builders of submarines and also constructed surface warships up to the size of cruisers. The yard's workmanship was of the highest class and was undertaken carefully and with precision. The yard had been modernised to a degree but not to the extent of Lithgows' Kingston Yard.

Lithgows consisted of two shipyards. Kingston Yard, the larger of the two, had been extensively modernised in 1961 and was then able to construct oil tankers up to 60,000 tons deadweight. This work had involved lengthening and widening of berths together with the provision of new steelwork shops equipped with the most modern machinery as well as a large prefabrication shed. The East Yard had had little money spent on modernisation. Its four berths were limited to building ships of up to 500 feet in length.

Unlike Scotts', Lithgows were builders of mainly tramp steamers, ore carriers and oil tankers and many of these were built in series. Their customers were world-wide particularly from Norway and India. Included among their customers were a number of U.K. owners who returned to the yard again and again for new ships—Shell, B.P., Denholm Line Steamers, Lyle Shipping Company and others. This applied also to their foreign clients—A. F. Klaveness and Jebsen of Norway and to their good friends from Bombay—Scindia Steam Navigation and the Mogul Line. The ships they built were rugged and they were built at speed. Lithgows regularly topped the River Clyde launching output for the year.

Unlike Scotts', they did not operate an engine works. although two engine works, those of John G. Kincaid of Greenock and David Rowan of Glasgow were financially tied in with the Lithgow Group.

Ferguson Bros., located up river from the Lithgow yards, built specialised craft up to about 350 feet in length including dredgers, tugs, small ferries, etc. Scott & Sons (Bowling) Ltd., built vessels of up to 235 feet in length.

While there can be little doubt that this merger provided the two main participants with a wider market, the main attraction of the agreement was the creation of a facility at Lithgows which would allow it access to the booming supertanker market. In due course the Glen Yard emerged in an area occupied by the defunct yard of William Hamilton and part of the berth area of Kingston Yard. The new building berth was straddled by a 225 ton gantry crane and was long enough to construct a supertanker in halves.

Lithgows had a long pedigree in tanker construction, having between the wars built tankers of 12,000 tons deadweight and as sizes began to escalate post-war, kept pace with this process. Prior to the merger, as already noted, they were building tankers of up to 60,000 tons deadweight. It was a tragedy when, only a few years following the opening of the Glen Yard, the tanker market collapsed.

The four companies forming the Scott Lithgow Group operated much as they had prior to merging, but in the case of Lithgows, the labour force grew in response to the size of the ships being constructed. Despite the excellent facilities, the build-cycle time never achieved its full potential. Whereas Swan Hunter, with inferior facilities, were building supertankers in exactly 12 months, the Glen Yard required considerably longer. It can only be a matter for conjecture whether the level of productivity had fallen in sympathy with the situation at U.C.S. or whether the sheer numbers of labour involved made the task of supervision more difficult. In any event, the combination of increased fixed overheads (reflecting the considerable investment) and slow cycle times was surely a recipe for trading losses. The Glen Yard's output of supertankers was restricted to four vessels, delivered two years apart, from 1974 to 1980.

In 1975, the dry cargo shipping market went into decline (and was not to recover until 1990). Orders were difficult to obtain and so Scott Lithgow took the bold decision to build a hugely complex semi-submersible emergency support vessel for B.P. They were encouraged by their earlier success in constructing the dynamically-positioned drillship BEN OCEAN LANCER for Ben Odeco in 1977. This vessel was built by Scotts'.

SWAN HUNTER GROUP

On the North East coast, talks were already underway in 1966 between Swan, Hunter and Wigham Richardson Ltd., on the Tyne and Smith's Dock Co. Ltd., which operated on both the Tyne and the Tees. Agreement to merge was reached while discussions were taking place with the other four shipbuilding companies on the River Tyne. In June 1967, all companies stated that agreement had been reached to form a group and that they planned to begin operations by January 1968. The new company was stated to have a potential output of 400,000 tons per annum and would employ some 15,000 people. Swan Hunter would have the majority interest.

Meanwhile the S.I.B. had in mind a Tyne/Tees group that would include the Haverton Hill Yard located on the Tees and the only yard not included in the Swan Hunter proposals. No agreement was reached between the S.I.B. and the Swan Hunter Group for the absorption into the Group of the Haverton Hill Yard. Shortly after Swan Hunter Group commenced operations in January 1968, it was announced that the Haverton Hill Yard would close, involving the loss of 2,000 jobs. The S.I.B. again requested that Swan Hunter Group investigate the possibility of taking over the yard and after a grant of £1 million had been made available the Haverton Hill Shipyard was absorbed into the Group.

In some ways the form that this merger took was similar to Scott Lithgow. No new headquarters was built and the board were all shipbuilders (apart from accountants). The design and estimating office was centralised, as was planning and industrial relations. Production was organised as before with production directors in each yard reporting to the board member for production. Neither Group, however, appeared to make any significant reductions in staff nor to eliminate duplicate facilities, which in theory at least should have been a source of potential savings in building costs. It has to be said, however, that the similarity ended there. Scott Lithgow employed the vast majority of its workers in two yards. Swan Hunter Group employed its 15,000 people across five yards on the Tyne, two on the Tees and two small shipyards—none of them employing much more than 2,000 people. A yard employing less than 2,000 is a reasonably compact unit, easier to control than one employing say 5,000. Of the seven main yards of Swan Hunter, only two had been modernised to any great extent — the Wallsend Yard, now capable of constructing supertankers and the Haverton Hill Yard, now capable of constructing oil-bulk/ore vessels up to 170,000 tons deadweight. The facilities of the other five yards were pretty poor by any standard.

The River Tyne's first supertanker, the ESSO NORTHUMBRIA of 253,000 tons deadweight, makes her way to sea. Built by Swan Hunter Shipbuilders Ltd. for Esso Petroleum in 1970.   *Builders' photograph*

LONDON CAVALIER — an S.D.14 cargo ship of 9,210 gross tons built for London & Overseas Freighters by Austin & Pickersgill Ltd. in 1972.   *W.S.P.L.*

In the 70s, the Glen yard built a series of supertankers in halves, while the Wallsend yard built a similar series in the conventional manner. As already noted, the facilities at Lithgow's Glen yard were superior to those at Wallsend, but the productivity was less. Scotts' yard built submarines, the occasional Royal Fleet Auxiliary vessel, together with merchant ships. Swan Hunter's Neptune yard on the Tyne built guided missile destroyers, the occasional Royal Fleet Auxiliary vessel, together with merchant ships. The workloads of these two yards bore a striking similarity but the shipyard facilities at Neptune yard were poor with craneage limited to 30 tons safe working load. Yet this shipyard delivered two guided missile destroyers, four fast cargo liners and a 24,000 tons gross cruise liner within a four year period.

The Swan Hunter yards were run on a "shoe-string". For example. the tanker berth at the Wallsend yard was equipped with three 60 ton hammerhead travelling cranes. These were used in tandem where appropriate but one or two lifts at the fore end of a supertanker were, at 50 tons, beyond the permitted safe working load at the relevant crane's outreach. Lithgow's yard on the other hand was equipped with a massive and costly 225 tons gantry crane and was accordingly much better equipped to erect large units of a supertanker, but one wonders how many lifts on the ship exceeded 200 tons and how many times this 225 ton gantry was used for lifting aboard a bag of bolts!

It can be argued therefore that capital investment on a large scale and the formation of large shipbuilding groups do not guarantee commercial success. The Swan Hunter Group constructed a wide variety of ship types and had they modernised with a view to building specific products, it could well be argued that they would have found it much more difficult to obtain sufficient orders to absorb their huge capacity.

HARLAND & WOLFF LTD.

This company remained separate post-Geddes and was modernised with a specific product in mind. The Belfast shipyard undertook a massive scheme of reconstruction with a building dock large enough to construct a million ton deadweight oil tanker and with steelwork facilities to match. A total of only twelve 260,000 ton supertankers were constructed at Belfast due to the market collapse of 1973. It is difficult however to see how the cost of building these would be less than the cost of building similar vessels at Swan Hunter's Wallsend yard. The reason is simple arithmetic. Unless the increase in fixed overheads equates to a decrease in direct labour costs, then the yard with the higher overheads will be less competitive. It is suggested that while Swan Hunter's labour costs were not higher than those at Belfast, their overheads were substantially lower.

The financial crises which this company encountered around this time are dealt with in due course.

AUSTIN & PICKERSGILL LTD.

This company was a very different kettle of fish but, like Harland & Wolff, remained separate post-Geddes. The management rightly foresaw the need to replace the huge number of Liberty ships constructed in the U.S.A. during wartime and sold world-wide after the war ended. The S.D.14 was designed to be cheap in first-cost and highly economical in service. The management also foresaw the trend away from tramp ships to bulk carriers and designed a series of bulk carriers. A & P got its timing right and no fewer than 126 S.D.14s were built at the yard, with 81 others built under licence elsewhere. A number of standard bulk carriers were also constructed. Despite the Geddes recommendations, the yard did not at first merge with its neighbours on the River Wear but was a huge success story. In August 1968 Austin & Pickersgill and Bartrams agreed to merge and following this agreement A & P bought the entire share capital of Bartrams.

Incidentally, the designation S.D.14 is generally believed to stand for "Standard Design, 14,000 tons deadweight". This is not the case however. The "S.D." represents the first last and letter of "Sunderland", although the 14 does refer to the tonnage.

DOXFORD & SUNDERLAND SHIPBUILDING & ENGINEERING CO. LTD.

Prior to publication of the Geddes report the three yards of J. L. Thompson, Sir James Laing and William Doxford had amalgamated to form the Doxford & Sunderland Shipbuilding & Engineering Co. Ltd. (later called Sunderland Shipbuilders).

The S.I.B. wished to see the three shipbuilding companies on the Wear — that is Austin & Pickersgill, Bartrams and Doxford & Sunderland—join forces. The three companies concerned could not accept this proposal. Some time later the S.I.B. announced that no further credit guarantees could be allowed in respect of new ships ordered with River Wear yards. This decision affected a number of potential orders and the companies made their objections known to the Ministry of Technology who promptly reinstated the guarantees.

Sunderland Shipbuilders through the 60s and up to nationalisation continued to operate three yards—Pallion, North Sands and Deptford (previously Doxford, J. L. Thompson and Sir James Laing respectively). The two latter were modernised in the early 60s—in the case of J. L. Thompson one berth was greatly extended.

The record of the North Sands and Deptford yards in the ten years prior to nationalisation is impressive for the very reason that neither was a "ship factory". Yet both competed successfully with Japanese and other foreign shipbuilders, many of whom had laid out "ship factories".

As tanker sizes rapidly escalated in the early 60s, the North Sands yard was able to participate fully in the tanker boom. By 1963, tankers of 85,000 tons deadweight were being constructed. Ship sizes continued to grow and by the early 70s, with a further berth extension, North Sands turned their hand to giant bulk carriers exceeding 150,000 tons deadweight. The Deptford yard was somewhat constrained from expanding its facilities but was still able to accommodate vessels up to 70,000 tons deadweight.

NAESS CRUSADER — a 150,000 tons deadweight bulk carrier built by Sunderland Shipbuilders Ltd. in 1973.   *W.S.P.L.*

The Liquefied Petroleum Gas Tanker HESIOD (ex GAMBADA) of 21,300 gross tons built by Cammell Laird (Shipbuilders) Ltd. in 1973.   *J. Y. Freeman.*

ROBB CALEDON SHIPBUILDERS LTD.

In May 1968 Henry Robb Ltd. of Leith and the Caledon Shipbuilding & Engineering Co. Ltd. of Dundee announced that they were merging to form Robb Caledon Shipbuilders Ltd. The S.I.B. approved the terms of the merger and made a grant of £400,000 available for modernisation work.

In order to deal with an expanding order book, the company acquired the assets of the Burntisland Shipbuilding Company which had closed the previous year. Thereafter steel fabrication began at Burntisland although the berths there remained empty.

APPLEDORE SHIPBUILDERS LTD.

This company was a success story and like Austin & Pickersgill, it was laid out as a totally enclosed "ship factory" able to construct relatively high-technology ships of up to around 5,000 tons deadweight. It did not, however, rely upon one specific product but on a variety of smaller vessels including mini container ships, dredgers, etc. Demand for these types of vessel was more stable than the market for bulk carriers and general cargo ships. Like Austin & Pickersgill, this company did not merge with another shipbuilder at this time.

OTHER YARDS

The two large yards of Vickers-Armstrongs at Barrow and Cammell Laird at Birkenhead remained separate, as did Vosper Thornycroft, together with a number of smaller yards.

ORDER BOOM

In 1967 the Labour Government devalued sterling which made U.K. prices more competitive. Following the second closure of the Suez Canal in 1967, a boom in ordering occurred and U.K. shipbuilders, many of whom had short order books, were able to offer early deliveries. For the fifteen months ending in December 1968, U.K. yards booked orders totalling no less than 3.2 million tons deadweight. World demand for ships remained at a high level in 1969 and 1970 and U.K. yards benefited from this situation. Unfortunately, most of this work was taken on a fixed price basis and in the years immediately following substantial losses were recorded by many companies.

LABOUR PRODUCTIVITY

Over the period of three decades, a steady decline in the attitude and behaviour of shipyard labour towards the use of the working day and to productivity generally has been noted. What is perhaps surprising is that one found that this decline started earlier in some shipbuilding centres than others. There was no question that, in the early 60s, output per man was higher and wage rates lower in Lithgows Ltd. than they were for example in John Browns. This remained true until shortly after the formation of Upper Clyde Shipbuilders in 1968. The increases in wage rates conceded by U.C.S. to its labour force soon resulted in a widening of the differential in wage rates between the Upper and Lower Clyde, which inevitably led to demands for parity by Lower Clyde workers. Although parity was not achieved, the attitude of the Lower Clyde workers was probably hardened by the spectacle and apparent success of the "work-in" staged by Upper Clyde Shipbuilders' workers following the company going into receivership in 1971. Another factor could have been the need, some years later, to recruit large numbers of steelworkers, not available locally, for the construction of supertankers and later, offshore structures. Such labour as was recruited had experience in offshore construction work and very high wages were paid to compensate such men for the spartan conditions prevailing on the construction sites in the West Highlands of Scotland. These spartan conditions were not a feature of the Scott Lithgow Group.

In any event, by the early 70s, the Lower Clyde labour force, insofar as productivity was concerned, became a mirror image of what their brethren on the Upper Clyde had been a decade earlier.

At the end of 1969 the Swan Hunter labour force was far more productive and co-operative than their counterparts on the Upper and Lower Clyde— and their wage rates were lower. They, too, became more militant and less productive when the industry was nationalised in 1977. The same change for the worse occurred in the yards on the Tees and the Wear, although it was not until the early 80s that a similar deterioration set in on these rivers.

Appledore Shipbuilders Ltd., from start-up until some time after nationalisation, enjoyed a labour force recruited and trained locally, untouched by the war-torn labour forces of other yards hundreds of miles away.

The later drop in productivity in the Wear and Tees yards and to a lesser extent on the Tyne compared to the Clyde may help to explain the success of Austin & Pickersgill, Sunderland Shipbuilders, Smith's Dock and Swan Hunter in the years leading up to nationalisation.

It is not in the least surprising that by the time the industry had been nationalised for two years or so, the speed of the convoy was the speed of the slowest ship and the wage rates were the rates of the highest paid in the industry. But prior to this debilitating process occurring, the yards that were most productive for longest were mostly to be found on the North East Coast, the majority of whom employed less than 2,000 people in each yard.

As already mentioned, the facilities of 5 of the 7 yards of the Swan Hunter Group (excluding the two small yards) were poor by the standards of the time. In 1968 when the Group was formed, Swan Hunter's management made no attempt to modernise the facilities of any of these 5 yards. Instead they concentrated on improving still further the steel work facilities of their Wallsend Yard by the provision of first, a computerised "panel-line" for flat steel units and second, heavier berth craneage. The thinking behind this strategy almost certainly was that when the next market downturn came and retrenchment became the order of the day, one or more of the poorly equipped yards would be sacrificed. In any case, each of these 5 yards would have required fundamental and costly modernisation to bring it up to scratch.

When the Wallsend yard improvements were complete, Swan Hunter then embarked upon the construction of a brand new steel preparation and fabrication facility on the site of the Palmers Hebburn dock, closed in 1970. This became known simply as Hebburn Dock and was equipped with a number of 100 ton cranes around the dock itself.

During the nine year life of the Swan Hunter Group up to the time when the industry was nationalised, the yards built virtually every type of ship except submarines and dredgers. Ships were allocated to the yards best suited to their construction and where possible, runs of sister ships were placed there in order to obtain the benefit of "learning curves". For example, the Wallsend yard built eight consecutive supertankers and the Haverton Hill yard built six 170,000 tons deadweight O.B.Os over this period. Vickers' Naval Yard built four container ships amongst other vessels, while the Hebburn yard built three Royal Fleet Auxiliaries, three liquefied petroleum gas tankers, three chemical tankers and two products tankers.

The references above to the steady decline in labour productivity were only made in general terms. What was of crucial importance was, of course, the effect of this decline in terms of manufactured cost and failure to deliver ships by the contracted date. The latter was probably the more serious because the reputation and credibility of some U.K. yards was, by the early 60s, beginning to be questioned by customers.

JAPAN ENTERS THE SOPHISTICATED SHIPBUILDING MARKET

At this time, Japanese shipyards were building mainly tankers and bulk carriers, the types of vessel considered relatively simple to construct. Shipbuilders in the U.K. considered that the Japanese would not be able to undertake the construction of more sophisticated types of ship and that the fact that Japanese output had begun to overtake the U.K. output did not, by itself, constitute a threat.

Two things happened to change these perceptions. First, the Japanese turned their hand to building more complex vessels and these were built to high standards and on time. Second, U.K. built ships continued to be delayed in delivery. By the late 60s, the U.K. shipbuilding industry had lost a good deal of its once-proud reputation, so far as timely delivery and price were concerned.

MATERIAL COSTS

As noted earlier, a number of U.K. yards were forced to close in the early 60s. This in turn affected the suppliers to the shipbuilding industry. They too, began to contract, albeit slowly at first. By the late 60s, the number of suppliers vying for business had fallen and this was particularly important for the larger elements making up the material content of a ship—main engines, deck cranes, hatch covers and the like. Steel by this time was only available in the U.K. from the British Steel Corporation, unless one bought German or Belgian steel for example and paid for its shipment to the subject shipyard. Even had this option been cheaper, the discharging of several thousand tons of steel from a coaster lying alongside a shipyard fitting-out jetty and then transporting it to a steel stockyard would prove for most shipyards to be impracticable.

Despite the growing lack of competition among U.K. suppliers, it is suggested that much tougher negotiations should have taken place with the suppliers. After all, since material costs represented around two-thirds of the total ship cost, a 10% reduction in material costs could have lowered ship selling prices by 6.5%. Japanese selling prices at this point were 10/20% lower than ours, with a few notable U.K. exceptions.

It is submitted therefore that the 60s represented the beginning of the real decline of the U.K. shipbuilding industry. While U.K. tonnage output as a percentage of world output fell from about 15% to around 5% over the decade, the success of Austin & Pickersgill and Appledore deserves great credit. Success in this context means profitability—the normal criteria for measurement of commercial success. Some have suggested that U.K. shipbuilders planned for stability and neglected growth and that this policy invited extinction.

As has been noted earlier, the huge increase in shipbuilding world capacity outgrew demand and led in the 70s to massive price cutting and to subsidies as governments attempted to avoid closures and large scale unemployment. To have embarked on a policy of shipbuilding expansion in the 60s could only have led to "profitless prosperity".

UPPER CLYDE SHIPBUILDERS COLLAPSE

Prior to the election of the Conservative Government in 1970, the Tories had stated their belief in a policy of non-intervention in Industry. This policy was seen to be applied by the refusal of further aid for U.C.S. which caused its immediate collapse in June 1971. No sooner was the announcement made of the company's liquidation than a protest campaign was mounted by Councillors, Trade Union officials and Shop Stewards. A deputation lobbied Parliament and delegations met the Prime Minister and the Minister for Trade & Industry.

Government's response was to appoint a committee to carry out a feasibility study as a matter of urgency for the purpose of establishing whether or not merchant shipbuilding could be made viable in the Upper Clyde. Meanwhile the liquidator appointed to wind up U.C.S. was receiving Government funds to pay the wages of those whom he had not made redundant and for materials.

The committee quickly made their recommendations which were:
1. U.C.S. to be liquidated.
2. Establish a successor to U.C.S. concentrated at Govan and Linthouse, while at the same time closing Clydebank and Scotstoun.
3. Existing shipbuilding programme to be as far as possible concentrated at Govan.
4. Government to assist the redeployment of those made redundant.

The Government accepted the report whereupon the workers (including those who had been made redundant) "occupied" Clydebank shipyard. This became known as the "work-in". Although only some 400 men had been made redundant, the fact that they turned up at the yard each day received massive media coverage.

GOVAN SHIPBUILDERS LTD.

In September 1971 Govan Shipbuilders was established and from its inception was totally funded by Government. The shop stewards refused to meet the new management and insisted that all four yards had to remain open. After further discussion it was conceded that Scotstoun could join Govan and Linthouse in forming Govan Shipbuilders while the Government would try to find a buyer for Clydebank.

EMERGING SHIP TYPES

In 1967, in response to the rise in port costs and dock labour problems, container ships made their appearance. The enormous cost of these large and fast ships could not be borne by individual shipping companies and consortia were formed in order to provide the financial muscle power. The two largest of these in the U.K. were Overseas Containers Ltd. (O.C.L.) and Associated Container Transportation (Australia) Ltd. (A.C.T.[A]). By 1967, Japanese shipbuilders had proved themselves capable of building all types of sophisticated ships but in the event, the orders for these ships were all placed in West Germany—five by O.C.L. and two by A.C.T.[A]. Over the next ten years or so, no less than twelve even larger vessels were ordered by O.C.L. and five by A.C.T.[A], all but one in West Germany. The single vessel was built by Swan Hunter. These vessels ranged in size from 21,000 up to 40,000 tons deadweight.

Apart from Swan Hunter who built five further medium-sized container ships and Smith's Dock at Middlesbrough (part of Swan Hunter Group) who built eight smaller container ships for Manchester Liners, two for Blue Star Line and one for Andrew Weir, and Fairfield who built one medium-sized container ship, U.K. shipbuilders totally missed out on this class of vessel.

The same applied to liquefied petroleum gas tankers as, except for a few built by Swan Hunter and Cammell Laird, U.K. shipbuilders missed out on this class of ship also. Similar remarks apply to the construction of liquefied natural gas and chemical tankers. Only one each of the former were built in the mid-60s by Harland & Wolff and Vickers and three of the latter were built by Swan Hunter in the 70s.

Very few ro-ro vessels have been built in the U.K., apart, that is, from small coastal ferries, despite the fact that such vessels were beginning to supplant the conventional cross-channel ferry and take over some of the routes covered by cargo liners.

A similar fate overtook cruise liner construction. The last pure passenger liners were built in the U.K. in the early 60s—two for Union-Castle and one each for P&O and the Orient Line. Thereafter pure passenger liners were rendered redundant by the jet airliner. From the mid-60s until the end of the decade, ships of this type were ordered basically as cruise ships but operating a liner service for a small part of each year. Only two such vessels were built in the U.K.—the KUNGSHOLM for Swedish America Line in 1966 and the QUEEN ELIZABETH 2 for Cunard in 1969, both by John Brown. Both incurred huge building losses. The last passenger ship built in the U.K. was the cruise ship VISTAFJORD, delivered to Norwegian America Line in 1973 by Swan Hunter. In the 70s, the cruising business took off and passenger ship construction was reborn. The U.K. shipbuilding industry played no part in this.

Container ships, gas tankers, ro-ros and cruise ships constitute the sophisticated end of modern shipbuilding and Britain, which in the 40s and 50s prided itself on the construction of sophisticated tonnage was now, Swan Hunter apart, barely involved. Japan by contrast, whose shipbuilding in the 50s had been confined to the construction of simpler vessels like tankers and cargo ships, was now in the sophisticated shipbuilding market with a vengeance.

By the 70s the bulk of the U.K. merchant shipbuilding industry, again Swan Hunter apart, was confined to building tankers, bulk carriers and cargo ships with a minority building reefer ships, small ferries, dredgers and other specialised craft. So it came to pass that U.K. shipbuilders, who had espoused the policy of product variety for the years following the end of World War II, found themselves left with only the rump! How did this happen?

There were two reasons. First, the fact that just when Japan was demonstrating its ability to build sophisticated ships of quality to time and price, U.K. shipbuilders were displaying an ever increasing tendency to deliver ships late. The fact that in 1967, the U.K. container ship consortia were not ready to place large contracts in Japan but quite content to place them in West Germany, showed that they were unwilling to place them in the U.K. As the years passed, they were persuaded to place such orders in Japan. It is probable therefore that in the field of container ships, U.K. shipbuilders were not asked to quote. It is also probable that similar remarks apply to gas tankers and large ro-ros.

The Government commissioned an independent study of the industry and the findings were published in 1972. The so-called Booz Allen Report correctly made the point that U.K. shipbuilders tended to respond to owners' enquiries but made little effort to gather market information and still less to formulate from such information, a market strategy. Had they done so, they might well have known in advance of shipowners' intentions, but their poor delivery record would have ruled them out of contention, even as far as bidding was concerned. Second, in the matter of cruise ships, the bad experience of those U.K. builders able to construct such vessels almost certainly persuaded them to stay clear of this type of vessel.

Booz Allen took the view that the U.K. shipbuilders' willingness to construct virtually any type of vessel within the shipbuilder's capabilities was an incorrect strategy. Booz Allen also took the view that with a short order book, U.K.

shipbuilders obtained orders for ships basically unsuited for a yard's facilities. This is an "ivory tower" approach. Of all the alternatives, without doubt the worst is an empty shipyard, particularly one which has been modernised and has therefore increased its fixed overheads.

REVIEW

In the five years following publication of the Geddes Report and the formation of the S.I.B.. the changes in the structure and operation of the industry can be summarised as follows:

1. Government funding made available through the S.I.B. for mergers and, more importantly, for modernisation.
2. Declining productivity and increasing number of days lost through strikes leading to late deliveries and to losses.
3. Declining involvement with sophisticated tonnage.
4. Failure to secure lower prices from suppliers.

All of the above despite a buoyant shipping market.

Government finance up to 1971 was channelled through the S.I.B. but thereafter was allocated on a direct basis to specific companies. It is timely to look at the financial returns of the main U.K. merchant yards in the five years following publication of the Geddes Report. Booz Allen listed these as follows:

NET PROFIT BEFORE TAX (£000s)

	1967	1968	1969	1970	1971
Appledore	124	127	192	268	217
Austin & Pickersgill	(762)	187	1,829	1,829	1,889
Cammell Laird	853	1,354	(7,974)	(628)	(4,275)
Doxford & Sunderland	(28)	1,612	(1,238)	(2,800)	(1,318)
Govan		NOT APPLICABLE			
Harland & Wolff	(1.156)	(755)	(8,330)	(302)	(182)
Robb-Caledon	43	106	(238)	(617)	(504)
Scott Lithgow	312	129	(206)	(1,550)	(262)
Swan Hunter	N/A	217	(3,449)	(5,604)	549
TOTAL	(614)	2,977	(16,938)	(9,410)	(3,886)

Cammell Laird's losses from 1969 coincided with the completion of the Polaris submarine programme and prompted Government intervention, as noted later.

Swan Hunter's heavy losses in 1969 and 1970 was the result of constructing the first two of a series of supertankers. Thereafter the company made profits.

Harland & Wolff's continuing losses prompted Government intervention from 1970 onwards, as noted later.

The success of Appledore and Austin & Pickersgill is in marked contrast to the rest. It has been suggested that the reason for this was that each yard evolved a product strategy lacking at the others. This may be true up to a point, but in the case of A & P, the replacement of Liberty ships with a long line of S.D.14s was a "once in a lifetime" event; and in the case of Appledore, the small ship market held up rather better than that for larger vessels. As already noted, both yards enjoyed the benefit of highly productive labour forces at this time.

It has also been suggested that one of the main reasons for the decline of the industry was that it was too small in scale. This argument is not consistent with the figures noted above, at least for those two yards. Neither of them merged with others as recommended by Geddes and both were comparatively small, even by U.K. standards.

FINANCIAL REVIEW

The main reason for the others' poor financial performance was escalating costs, notably in labour and overheads, in relation to fixed price contracts. In the case of labour, although in 1967 shipbuilding wage rates compared favourably with those in the engineering industry and elsewhere in the U.K., in the five years under review, earnings grew by nearly 5% in real terms. Most of this could not be recovered from fixed price contracts; what was worse was the increasing occurrence of strikes, which compared badly with other industries. The 750 days lost per 1,000 employees in 1967 rose to a figure of 2,800 days lost in 1972. All this compounded the effect of lowering productivity to cause the cost per ton of manufacture to rise steeply. Fixed overheads were increased substantially in most yards by virtue of the modernisation schemes. Overheads were increased still further by employment-related overheads such as holiday pay and national insurance.

In many cases, working capital was wiped out and in the years 1970 and 1971 was negative. The industry became dependent upon grants and loans disbursed by the S.I.B. These had originally been intended for the formation and start-up costs of groups and for transitional losses, but was later changed to funds being made available for improved facilities. However, in the end much of it was used to provide working capital.

Of the £43 million disbursed between 1967 and 1972 by the S.I.B., Harland & Wolff received £15 million; U.C.S. received £12.8 million; Swan Hunter received £5.8 million and Scott Lithgow received £5.2 million.

The heavy losses at Cammell Laird between 1968 and 1971 caused the Government to take 50% of the equity of the shipbuilding company. For the same reason, the Northern Ireland Ministry of Commerce took a 47.6% share of the equity of Harland & Wolff for £4 million in 1970. In the case of Govan, the Government owned 100% of the equity from its inception in 1972.

Over the six year period ending in 1972, these three companies received massive injections of direct Government aid: U.C.S./Govan received no less than £52 million (of which £12 million was for capital expenditure), Harland & Wolff received £36.5 million (of which £21 million was for capital expenditure) and Cammell Laird received £21.5 million (of which £14 million was for capital expenditure).

The total aid made available to the industry over this period was a staggering £160 million (£43 million through the S.I.B. and £117 million by the D.T.I./N.I.Min. of Commerce). The three companies noted above received between them £138 million! It is clear that without direct Government aid these three companies would have gone under, and in three areas of high unemployment, the situation would have otherwise become much more serious. But that each of these three companies should receive between £12/21 million for capital expenditure seems a grotesque decision by Government. Their facilities were no worse than those of Doxford & Sunderland, for example, who received "peanuts" from the S.I.B. Moreover, the productivity levels were superior at Doxford & Sunderland. Strikes had plagued Cammell Laird for years and Govan was not noted particularly for its placid labour force.

The recommendations of Geddes in 1966 did not call for direct Government intervention, still less on the scale of the intervention that took place with individual companies between 1967/72. It is probable that such intervention was not the result of any policy but rather a series of ad-hoc decisions.

It was not even justified in terms of manpower. The three companies referred to received between them some 85% of all shipbuilding assistance (both by S.I.B. and by direct Government aid) in the five year period. They employed between them some 16,000 out of a total of some 49,000 in merchant shipbuilding — equivalent to about 33%!

It is interesting to compare the financial performance of the continental competition with that of the U.K. Booz Allen noted that the sales growth of the European yards examined was much better than the U.K. but that their financial performance was not significantly better. This is, of course, the key issue. Booz Allen went on to note that sales revenue per employee was higher in the continental yards as was the yards' level of capital expenditure and noted also that the advantages inherent in their modern facilities were offset by their higher labour costs. Booz Allen suggested that if capital expenditure in U.K. yards reached European levels, this should result in a competitive advantage. This in theory is possibly correct, but it was very different in practice. It is difficult to understand how Booz Allen could advance this proposition when elsewhere in their report they noted that in the U.K. there had been no evidence of a significant improvement in productivity from 1967 up to 1972—and this despite the massive injections of Government aid for this purpose noted earlier—totalling £160 million.

The most important point in the comparison remains the fact that despite their sales growth, the financial performance of the continental yards was little better than ours. There seems little point in sales growth if it leads to "profitless prosperity". But this, of course, was a direct result of the expansionist policies of almost all our foreign competitors. Having committed themselves to huge throughput potential, they were now obliged to fill this capacity.

Other comparisons with continental yards were just as interesting. Their staff to labour ratios were higher; their ratio of naval architects and engineers to the total design and drawing office staff was higher; the ratio of design and drawing office staff to the total workforce was higher. There can be little doubt that the U.K. builders' design and drawing office staffs were generally too few in number and this frequently resulted in late delivery of drawings for production with a consequent impact on costs and delays. Whether this was due to a reluctance by young people to join the staff of a shipyard or whether it was the fault of the shipbuilders themselves is open to question.

The average output per employee in the U.K. compared very badly with the continental yards examined. The figures were 28 gross registered tons per employee for the U.K. and a figure of 119 gross registered tons for Europe. These figures lead one to the conclusion that U.K. productivity or lack of it was the major contribution to the industry's decline.

Booz Allen considered that U.K. suppliers were highly competitive in both price and quality but displayed an unsatisfactory delivery record. Personal experience indicated a very different picture. There were numerous examples of foreign suppliers offering better designs and prices for deck cranes for example. The U.K. delivery record was not uniformly bad —some suppliers had consistently good delivery records.

FURTHER REVIEW

This then was the U.K. shipbuilding scene in the five years following publication of the Geddes Report.

The industry had been largely modernised but the fall in productivity had offset the benefits resulting from capital expenditure. The traditional links between U.K. owners and U.K. builders had been severed and the majority of these owners now contracted abroad. A number of groupings recommended by Geddes had been established but viability of the larger ones, Swan Hunter apart, had still not been achieved. There was no doubt that the decline of the industry was well underway. More and more foreign capacity was coming on stream. Brazil, Poland and Yugoslavia were all now in the "big league" and the growing might of South Korea and later China might even then be seen to pose a threat to the Japanese.

In 1973 the tanker market collapsed with the decision by the Organisation of Arab Petroleum Exporting Countries following the Yom Kippur War with Israel, to quadruple oil prices. Very large crude carriers began slow steaming and many went into lay-up. Shipyard contracts were cancelled. All the world's yards with the facilities to build these monsters were now in a quandary. In the U.K. only two yards, those of Harland & Wolff and Scott Lithgow had been laid out specifically for this purpose. In Scott Lithgow's case, at least the facilities were designed to build a V.L.C.C. in halves. Their shorter building berth could more economically accommodate other tonnage than the huge building dock at Belfast.

Swan Hunter, although able to construct a V.L.C.C. conventionally on their crossover building berth, had never laid out their Wallsend yard specifically to build this type and size of vessel. Their altogether more modest capital expenditure was now to prove an advantage.

CHAPTER 6

RUN-UP TO NATIONALISATION
1972—1977

For the next five years up to nationalisation of the industry in July 1977, the Government's direct involvement with specific shipbuilding companies continued.

In the case of Govan Shipbuilders, the Government announced financial support of £35 million in 1972 to last until the company reached viability. However, the yard modernisation scheme ran late, productivity did not improve and contract losses were announced. In 1975 the Government responded with a loan of £6.9 million together with further funds of £10.3 million to cover anticipated losses.

For Cammell Laird, as mentioned in Chapter 5, the Government provided funds prior to 1972 totalling £21.5 million of which £14 million was to cover modernisation. As with Govan, the modernisation scheme ran very late and at the same time the cost escalated. The company ran short of working capital and Government responded with funds totalling £6 million. The company then began to report modest profits.

Government intervention with Harland & Wolff took place on numerous occasions between 1971 and 1975 at which point it took over 100% of the assets. Finance was made available to cover losses, modernisation, replacement of debt with shares and guarantees and finally for writing off loans and for a financial reconstruction. Over £100 million was involved.

In order to assist the shipbuilding industry generally, Government introduced a system of Tapering Grants. These were set at a level of 10% of the value of contracts booked in 1972, 4% of the value of contracts booked in 1973 and 3% of the value of contracts booked in 1974. All this was embodied into the Industry Act 1972.

The Government intervened with other companies but to a much lesser degree. In 1974, Sunderland Shipbuilders was granted a loan of £9 million, subject to their parent — Court Line — investing £3 million, for the purpose of creating a "ship factory" at Pallion. Court Line, which also owned Appledore Shipbuilders as well as shipping and holiday interests, very suddenly got into financial difficulties. The urgent question now was how to fund the shipyard modernisation scheme. Government took an immediate decision to take the shipbuilding interests of Court Line into public ownership. Court Line itself thereafter collapsed. The new Pallion Yard was opened in 1975. In the same year, Austin & Pickersgill commenced a £27 million reconstruction programme which was completed in 1977 and which included a £9 million contribution from Government. Like the Pallion "ship factory" it was designed to permit production of ships in enclosed facilities. Whereas the Pallion layout

68

consisted of a fully enclosed shallow building dock with dock gates and was capable of building two ships simultaneously of around 30,000 tons deadweight, the Austin & Pickersgill layout consisted of a partially-enclosed building berth and adjoining stern section and block assembly hall and was capable of constructing standard vessels up to 35,000 tons deadweight.

They were both among the best shipbuilding facilities in Europe and it is revealing to note that the total cost of both to Government was restricted to £18 million.

In 1975 also, Robb Caledon announced losses arising from labour problems and contract losses. They were in fact rescued to the tune of £2.5 million, a sum guaranteed by the Post Office, one of the yard's customers.

In 1976, following the market slump in 1975, Austin & Pickersgill received a Government loan of £9 million required to cover gaps in its order book, which had resulted in overhead under-recovery.

In the same year Marathon, the rig builders at Clydebank (who had taken over the yard following the U.C.S. collapse), were obliged to lay off 1,000 men because of shortage of work. The Government approved the placing of a speculative jack-up drilling rig by British National Oil Corporation at a cost of £14 million.

The table below indicates the orders placed in U.K. yards over the 10 year period ending in 1975. The level fluctuated widely and the table clearly indicates the market collapse of 1975. It was not to improve substantially for a very long time. Thereafter, shipbuilders across the world fought head-to-head for the much reduced business available, while Governments subsidised their shipbuilding industries in a vain attempt to prevent large-scale unemployment. The "rat race" was well and truly begun.

ORDERS PLACED IN U.K. YARDS

Year	000s Gross Registered Tons
1966	482
1967	1,077
1968	2,565
1969	2,119
1970	1,769
1971	1,027
1972	839
1973	4,358
1974	862
1975	67

It is quite clear that between 1970 and 1974. the Conservative Government had set its face against the closure of Cammell Laird, Harland & Wolff and Govan Shipbuilders, despite its so-called policy of "non-intervention". The Labour Government elected in 1974 was committed to nationalisation of the industry. It was not surprising, with Govan 100% publicly owned, Cammell

M.V. ANDALUCIA STAR — a reefer vessel of 9,981 gross tons built for Blue Star Line Ltd. by Smith's Dock Co. Ltd. in 1975. *W.S.P.L.*

The 946 T.E.U. containership MANCHESTER VANGUARD built for Manchester Liners Ltd. by Smith's Dock Co. Ltd. in 1977. *Author's collection*

Laird 50% publicly owned and Harland & Wolff 47.6% publicly owned, that the Labour Government took Harland & Wolff into full public ownership in 1975. Nor was it surprising when, the year before, Sunderland Shipbuilders came into public ownership.

By contrast with the yards mentioned previously, Smith's Dock Co. Ltd. on the River Tees was a medium-sized yard able to construct ships up to about 35,000 tons deadweight. Its steelwork facilities in particular were positively antique. On the berth for example only two cranes were of the travelling variety—the rest were fixed. The plater's shed and fabrication shed were some distance apart and material handling was accordingly labour-intensive. The facilities had last been upgraded in the mid-50s. Since being taken over by Swan Hunter in 1968 it had had virtually no money invested in new plant.

Despite all this, in the four years prior to nationalisation the company recorded trading profits averaging £900,000 per annum on a turnover of some £20 million. The output during this period consisted of reefer ships, container ships and offshore supply boats.

Despite the high wages paid and the labour-intensive nature of the yard, productivity was excellent. Strikes were almost unknown. While there is a limit as to how long one can tolerate such outdated plant and equipment, there is surely a lesson to be learned from this experience.

Special mention should be made of Swan Hunter at this point. From 1971 up until nationalisation, it made modest profits. During this period, it entered into a partnership with Maritime Fruit Carriers of Israel and a new company— Swan Maritime—was formed. The intention was for this new company to order a series of ships all of which would be built by Swan Hunter and which would be chartered out. A number of tankers of 250,000 tons deadweight, 112,000 tons deadweight and 32,000 tons deadweight were in fact built. Unfortunately Maritime Fruit Carriers failed and Swan Hunter were left to sell a number of the tankers.

This huge shipbuilding group represented a sizeable percentage of U.K. merchant shipbuilding at this time. The sheer control that top management exerted over its complex affairs was something commanding respect. The various yards built all the types of vessels that the other large yards had not built—gas tankers and container ships for example. They were in addition the leading builder for the Royal Fleet Auxiliary as well as being established naval builders. It seems particularly sad that the talents of its top management were not brought to bear in the running of British Shipbuilders.

The market collapse of 1975 coincided with South Korea and China making their entry into shipbuilding. The potential of South Korea in particular was a frightening prospect. This was the scenario when Government appointed an Organising Committee in readiness for nationalisation. After delays in placing the necessary legislation on the Statute Book, the Shipbuilding Industry Act (1977) was finally passed and British Shipbuilders became a reality in July 1977.

CHAPTER 7

NATIONALISATION—THE LAST STRAW 1977—1988

In many respects, British Shipbuilders (BS) was similar to an enlarged UCS. The companies forming each organisation were of widely differing sizes and types, different management philosophies, different wage rates and some more highly modernised than others. They both contained naval builders and both began life with a poor order book. There the similarities stopped. BS included for example engine building and shiprepairing companies.

The shipping market had collapsed only two years previously and was to remain in this condition for the life of BS. This posed an intractable problem for the Corporation but their efforts to overcome it were anything but businesslike, as will become clear.

Set up under the Shipbuilding Industry Act (1977), BS was never allowed the freedom of action open to companies in the private sector and decision making was slow, since it was required to consult the officials of the Shipbuilding Policy Division of the Department of Trade & Industry (DTI) on all matters of importance. These officials numbered some 65 and so BS was monitored in considerable detail.

The principal instrument for this monitoring process was the 5 year rolling Corporate Plan which BS was under a statutory duty to provide each year to Government. This document was considered of paramount importance by both parties but the problem was, quite simply, that it was impossible to predict future levels of ordering, prices, wage rates, productivity and overheads (from which turnover and profit/loss were predicted) even for 12 months ahead, far less 4 years. As has been shown, the market can rise or fall overnight, affected as it is by world events like wars and crises of confidence. In any event, BS was measured against this document and unfortunately it was consistently proved to be optimistic in its forecasting, which one concludes did little to impress the DTI.

BS set up two headquarters— one in Newcastle housing all its staff except marketing and the other in Knightsbridge housing marketing staff together with a small Press Office. Board Members appointed by the Secretary of State for the DTI had offices in both H.Qs.

By the time recruitment of H.Q. staff was completed, several hundred were involved. The overhead costs incurred were considerable and were, of course, in addition to the existing overheads in the subsidiaries. The H.Q. staff in Newcastle covered the functions of finance, industrial relations, legal and corporate planning, but very significantly not technical.

The trouble with a large H.Q. staff is the size of its demands for information and this was particularly marked in the case of the Finance Department. So, too, became the demands of the Corporate Planning Department some 3/4 months before the next Corporate Plan was due each year. Thus was generated a good deal of paperwork which the smaller subsidiaries, in particular, were not geared up to produce.

The Marketing Department was not large but its members travelled extensively in their attempts to make known the features of BS — its subsidiaries' sizes and capabilities and their product range. Although in some cases their efforts were perhaps misdirected, in the sense that some countries visited had no hope of financing new construction, they were generally correct because, in the Third World in particular, shipowners had but a hazy idea of the newly-formed BS. Marketing was a function that had never been universally practised by yards under private ownership. After the flight of U.K. shipowners to foreign shipbuilders in the 60s it was doubly important to undertake marketing.

With the BS set-up in place, the individual constituents of the Corporation were left very much to themselves, apart from the provision of reports to H.Q. In short, they were treated as subsidiaries. But all the merchant shipbuilding yards, engine builders and shiprepairers were very short of work. In fact, only 77,000 tons gross of new orders were placed in the U.K. for the first nine months of 1978. This followed the tragic year of 1975 when a meagre 67,000 tons gross was placed and by two indifferent years following this insofar as ordering was concerned. This situation led to about 3,000 redundancies spread across the merchant yards.

BS, in its first Corporate Plan presented to Government in May 1978, considered a number of options insofar as merchant shipbuilding was concerned:

1. Retain current capacity.
2. Almost total withdrawal from merchant shipbuilding.
3. Reduction in capacity of 32% with the loss of 12,300 jobs.

Option 3 was the BS preferred option.

It was at this point that the Labour Government promoted a scheme designed to secure a large order for BS. A joint company was set up between BS and the Polish Steamship Company who then ordered 22 bulk carriers and 2 crane barges with BS. The Polish Steamship Company thereafter chartered these ships for 15 years. Negotiations were concluded and contracts duly signed, the prices benefiting from the Intervention Fund subsidy introduced by Government prior to nationalisation. Not only did BS sustain a large financial loss on completion of the shipbuilding programme, but it is believed that the British taxpayer paid much more in addition. The level of the charter rates involved has never been divulged!

Around the same time, Sunderland Shipbuilders concluded negotiations with the Shipping Corporation of India for six cargo vessels. These were, with the approval of Government, designated part of the Aid Package available to India. They also benefited from the Intervention Fund subsidy. Not only was the gift subsidised but the yard recorded a loss on the contract!

73

This work only provided relief to a few of the merchant yards, many of whom were recording under-recovery of overheads due to their work shortages. This was a feature of BS operations that it consistently failed to address adequately.

When a shipyard, or any business come to that, runs short of work, it becomes necessary, of course, to shed a proportion of its labour force. But fixed overheads are no longer being fully recovered and so the business records a loss. In the case of the merchant shipbuilders, not only were they shedding labour and recording losses through under-recovered overheads but they were recording contract losses on their ships as well.

BS should have exercised control over this situation by immediately reducing capacity by closing one or more yards. In fact the first yard to close was that of Haverton Hill in 1979, but that was at the request of its parent, Smith's Dock, who considered that the poor industrial relations record at Haverton Hill could pose a threat to its own survival.

At this time, and indeed for almost all the life of BS, merchant yards were in fact competing against one another, as well as foreign competition, for the little business available. The reasons that contract losses were being recorded were not just lowering productivity and rising wages in relation to fixed prices but also, curiously enough, because of the Intervention Fund subsidy.

This subsidy had been introduced by Government prior to nationalisation for the purpose of enabling U.K. shipbuilders to match Far East prices. It operated thus: A fixed amount of subsidy was made available to the industry over a period of say one year. From this "pot", yards could bid their break-even price to which they then applied the subsidy at a level fixed by Government (20%-30% variation over the years).

This system gave rise to a number of problems. First, the subsidy (i.e. the 20%—30%) was never large enough to bridge the gap between a U.K. and a Far East price. Accordingly in some cases, a price less than break-even was quoted which with subsidy applied, could win the business. Hence contract losses were recorded. Second, two or more U.K. yards usually quoted for the same business and their break-even prices were, of course, different. BS then had to decide who would get the business. The yard with the lowest break-even price required the least subsidy and by applying this principle over the life of the "pot" more contracts could be won. BS, in fact, on occasion allowed a yard with a higher break-even price to win the business because otherwise it might run out of work.

There was in short no strategy for dealing with capacity at this point in time. When the orders forecast in the current Corporate Plan were not forthcoming, the BS remedy was limited to redundancies.

Each yard tried to obtain new business utilising its own designers and estimators and, when successful, its own drawing office. No attempt was made by the Corporation to centralise the design and estimating functions. Had they done so, as Swan Hunter Group did when it was first formed, BS would have found it much easier to control the destiny of individual yards. They did, it is true, control the allocation of subsidy without which no new work could be obtained and by this means could have starved an individual yard if their intention had been to close it. By centralising design and estimating from the outset, however, BS could have allocated new tonnage to the yards as they pleased. In any event, two or more U.K. yards competing for the same business was a waste of valuable technical resources.

Since the market was so poor, most of the yards were anything but full and this had two consequences. First, productivity slipped as employees saw their last ship nearing completion. Second, overheads were not being fully recovered.

With a large design and estimating department in the heart of the Corporation working presumably for a Board Member for Naval Architecture (a position never created), BS could have selected which yards would have to be sacrificed and cram the rest with work. Overheads could then have been much more fully recovered.

It has already been noted how, in the late 60s and early 70s, most U.K. shipbuilders missed out on container ships, cruise ships, gas tankers and ro-ros and were left to build tankers, bulk carriers, cargo ships and reefers. The BS marketing team had the resources to do what in private hands shipbuilders had never done —namely, to identify market trends and specific ship types needed to satisfy these. It was not until some years had passed that BS tried to market standard ships and allocate each type of notional ship to individual yards. The ships themselves were not, however, within the categories that had been missed out previously. As a result, BS found itself competing with virtually every shipbuilder in the world for tankers, bulk carriers and cargo ships.

This is a far cry from the experience at Wartsila of Finland, for example, who identified a growing demand for cruise ships. The company dominated this market segment for more than a decade, although they were not previously noted for building highly sophisticated ships of this type. There seems little doubt that good prices were obtained for these ships, so dominant was the company in this field. Similar remarks apply to Moss Rosenberg of Norway in relation to gas tankers.

In July 1977, the total number employed by the Corporation was some 87,000. By 1981 this was down to 69,500. Financial losses were being recorded in all the merchant yards, in Scott Lithgow on offshore work and by the Shiprepair Division. Insofar as the latter was concerned, between 1981 and 1982 Tyne Shiprepair Limited was restructured twice with a grievous loss of jobs and closed premises.

Not long after nationalisation, a committee was set up to consider requests from subsidiaries for capital expenditure. Despite the continuing losses, approval was given for millions of pounds for new plant and machinery. A significant proportion was spent on computer technology. A company in private hands would, in these straitened circumstances, have placed a ban on such expenditure until the accounts could justify it.

The drillship PACNORSE I of 9,872 gross tons and with diesel-electric propulsion built for Pacnorse Drilling Corporation I by Scott Lithgow in 1979.   Mark Banavage

The Type 22 frigate H.M.S. BROADSWORD completed by Yarrow & Co. Ltd. in 1979.
Leo van Ginderen

So far as the unions were concerned, July 1977 was the realisation of their ambitions — state ownership. Their membership in the yards initially believed that they had a job for life! When one adds to this the disparate wage rates, one has a recipe for low productivity and strife.

The unions, despite their euphoria, were not idle. Under the Fair Wages Act, claims were successfully lodged for parity with the highest rates prevailing in any BS yard. Similar successful claims were lodged on behalf of staff.

In return for the unions agreeing to reduce the number of individual rates of wages across the Corporation, BS accepted that henceforth no employee could be made compulsorily redundant. Work was still very scarce and as a result BS was stuck with surplus employees enjoying enhanced wages, unless that is, they could be persuaded to accept voluntary redundancy. This concession proved to be highly expensive. Later, BS persuaded Government to introduce a special shipbuilding redundancy scheme with improved terms in an effort to resolve the situation.

In 1980, rumour was rife that the Conservative Government, elected the previous year, was going to privatise the naval yards. The huge losses being incurred by merchant shipbuilders, engine builders, offshore builders and shiprepairers was dwarfing the profits generated by the naval builders.

Around this time, in an effort to improve overall performance, a new BS department was created entitled Performance Improvement and Productivity (PIP). This department took under its wing computing, shipbuilding technology and working practices and a senior man was recruited to control it. From this point onwards, a bewildering series of changes were put into effect involving computer technology, working practices, quality engineering, planning and "produceability", core systems, training, product development and subcontracting.

Despite the implementation of Computer Aided Design/Computer Aided Manufacture involving inter alia considerable capital investment, drawings were still late on issue to production. Improvements in working practices were eventually secured, however. The Corporation referred to all of this as the management of change. While well named and laudable in its aim of creating the very best in modern management methods, it totally failed in two crucial areas—productivity and under-recovery of overheads.

Due to work shortages continuing, the 69,500 employed in March 1981 had fallen to 66,000 by March 1982 and to 64,000 a year later. These reductions were achieved through voluntary redundancy.

Nowhere had advanced technology been espoused more than at Scott Lithgow. Following completion of the emergency support vessel IOLAIR for B.P., albeit at a loss, the decision was taken to delve deeper into the offshore field and contracts were signed with both B.P. and Ben Odeco for semi-submersible drilling rigs.

Prior to this, the company had secured an order for a 128,000 tons deadweight tanker from B.P. Because IOLAIR was late in delivery this caused the tanker to be late also and both incurred delivery penalties.

Regrettably both drilling rigs were late and incurred severe penalties.

Resulting mainly from the Lithgow as distinct from the Scott contracts, the company recorded very serious losses over a number of years especially in both 1983 and 1984.

BS established that managements at the three unprofitable repair yards of Tyne Shiprepair, Vosper Shiprepairers and Grangemouth Dockyard were prepared to buy the businesses and by 1984 these were sold. Around the same time, Government instructed BS to make arrangements to sell off its general engineering companies together with its profitable shiprepair operation at Falmouth. Instructions were also given to sell Scott Lithgow. In the financial year 1984/85 the majority of these companies had been privatised. From the 64,000 employed in 1983, staff and hourly paid employees in the Corporation dropped to 37,000 in 1984.

In July 1984, formal instructions were given by Government to privatise the warship yards and to complete these sales by March 1986. It seemed quite clear that Government intended to abandon merchant shipbuilding in the U.K. by gradually reducing the shipbuilding subsidy. This view was lent credence by the closure of Robb Caledon's two yards and the Scotstoun yard of Govan Shipbuilders between 1983 and 1984 and by the sale of Hall, Russell's yard early in 1985. The official BS line at the time was that, with the approval of Government, BS was setting out to achieve a "mainstream business of merchant ship and engine building".

It is perhaps timely at this point to state the losses, at trading level, reported by the Corporation from 1978 to 1984. These were as follows:

Year	Loss (£ million)
1978	104.5
1979	49.5
1980	109.9
1981	41.4
1982	19.7
1983	117.5
1984	160.9

These losses were recorded despite the substantial profits being generated by the warship builders and they were generally far greater than those forecast in the Corporate Plan issued 12 months previously.

In 1985, Government advised the Corporation that the 1985/86 Corporate Plan should be based on "reduced and degressive levels of financial support".

These levels were stated to be:

for 1985/86—£45 million;

for 1986/87 £35 million and

for 1987/88 £25 million.

When the 1985/86 Corporate Plan was issued to Government, it indicated a break-even position after subsidy for the three years in question. The results were very different.

In 1985 also, BS instituted "regionalisation of outfit manufacturing" in an effort to avoid duplication of facilities. Pipework manufacture, electrical installation and joinery work began to be centralised on Clydeside and in the North East of England—the areas where the bulk of the remaining shipyards were based. This process, of course led to a number of redundancies which, coming on top of earlier redundancies, resulted in an immediate further drop in morale.

During the year Yarrow Shipbuilders was sold while Sales Memoranda and Accountants' Reports were prepared and issued in respect of the other naval builders. In the meantime, Cammell Laird Shipbuilders became a subsidiary of Vickers Shipbuilding & Engineering Ltd.

After two years of severe decline in orders for merchant ships, 1984/85 saw sales rise 72% over the previous year, although total sales for the year still represented only 200,000 compensated gross tons. They included two major contracts, that of a 31,000 gross tons vessel for North Sea Ferries at Govan and a massive crane barge worth £50 million at Sunderland Shipbuilders.

In their Corporate Plan for 1985/86, BS confirmed that 22 merchant contracts had been secured totalling some 200,000 compensated gross tons. Such an order book could have been absorbed by say Swan Hunter (9 vessels), Ferguson-Ailsa (7 vessels—where they were actually built) and the remaining 6 in one other yard. In fact these 22 orders were spread across five yards. BS, in referring to these orders stated—". . . The pattern of order intake was concentrated in the latter half of the year giving rise to considerable capacity under-utilisation which will extend into 1985/86. This will be mitigated by a programme of redundancies supported by extensive lay-offs and temporary transfers between yards to an extent not previously achieved".

"Mitigated" it may have been, but the financial forecast detailed in the document indicates for merchant shipbuilding no less than £36 million under-recovery of overheads on a turnover of £179 million.

The position at the start of 1985/86 at each yard was as follows:

Austin & Pickersgill
2—North Sea barges
2—21,000 tons deadweight multi-purpose cargo ships

Ferguson-Ailsa
1—Ash disposal vessel
1—Small ferry
1—Arctic offshore vessel
2—Offshore supply boats
1—Research vessel
1—Vessel for Townsend Shipping

Govan Shipbuilders
3—Colliers of 19,000 tons deadweight each
1—31,000 tons gross ferry

Smith's Dock
41—Small barges
4—Cargo vessels of 15,000 tons deadweight each
1—Diving support vessel
Sunderland Shipbuilders
2—Large diving support vessels
1—Crane/accommodation barge

A number of these orders gave rise to severe technical problems which, combined with low fixed prices and onerous delivery penalties, caused heavy losses. For example, Austin & Pickersgill contracted two cargo vessels with Egon Oldendorff of Lubeck at fixed prices reflecting a forecast increase in productivity. This was not forthcoming and in addition, the vessels were late in delivery. In the case of Govan, the ferry, although delivered on time to North Sea Ferries, resulted in a huge contract loss. Smith's Dock ran into technical problems nearing completion of their diving support ship which incurred liquidated damages for late delivery as well as cost overruns. Finally, in the case of Sunderland Shipbuilders, the two highly sophisticated diving support ships for Stena Line of Sweden could not initially meet their specified technical features on trials and large losses were recorded due to the delays in overcoming these problems. The highly onerous contract payment terms only served to exacerbate the problem. At around the same time. the owners of the crane barge went into receivership leaving the yard with a partially constructed £50 million contract but no owner.

During 1985, all BS subsidiaries, with the exception of Govan Shipbuilders, reduced their labour forces as a result of work shortages, regionalisation and planned reductions in overheads. The Corporation announced its intention to close Smith's Dock and also announced the forthcoming merger of Austin & Pickersgill with Sunderland Shipbuilders. The new company was named North East Shipbuilders Limited—(NESL).

In 1986 the Corporation completed the sale of the naval builders together with Swan Hunter and Hall, Russell. The average numbers employed by BS fell from the 37,000 in 1984 to some 11,000 in 1985.

Shortly after North East Shipbuilders started trading on 1st April 1986, the company landed an order worth some £93 million for 24 small ferries for Danish interests. This was achieved despite the continuing weakness of the shipping market and provided two-thirds of the labour force with continuous employment until 1989. The difficulties encountered with the various contracts already mentioned were addressed by the new company— the technical problems with the Stena ships, the cost overruns and lateness with the Oldendorff ships and perhaps biggest of all—the "fire sale" of the crane barge.

Whereas between them, Sunderland Shipbuilders and Austin & Pickersgill had turned in losses of some £35 million for the year ending March 1986, the difficulties referred to served to escalate the losses. In its first full year of operation, NESL recorded a loss of £56 million.

The first of three 30,900 tons deadweight bulk carriers built for Nosira Shipping Ltd. in 1981 being floated out of the Pallion ship factory of Sunderland Shipbuilders Ltd.
"Sunderland Echo"

STENA SEAWELL — the first of two diving support ships built for Stena Line by North East Shipbuilders Ltd. in 1987.   *Author's collection*

It is timely to state the Corporation's losses from 1985 until it effectively ceased operations in 1989. These losses were:

Year	Loss (£ million)
1985	68.0
1986	136.9
1987	147.5
1988	109.9

Thus although BS had been cut down to six merchant yards, one engine builder and a handful of other small companies, the loss recorded in 1987 was the second highest since nationalisation ten years previously. This was largely the result of the operations at NESL and Govan Shipbuilders, wherein the bulk of the employees were working. The latter company recorded a loss that year of some £31 million.

The shipbuilding facilities at both Austin & Pickersgill and Sunderland Shipbuilders were among the finest in Europe. The 24 Danish ferries, it was believed, would provide an ideal workload. The ferries were of two classes (12 of each), but were in most respects very similar to each other. To obtain maximum benefit from series building, each yard was allocated the 12 ferries in each class.

Around the time of delivery of the first ferry, it was alleged by the owner that the ship did not fully meet the specification and he announced his intention of determining the contract. While discussions continued and legal advice was sought, the ferries continued building at each yard. Due to a shortage of work at Appledore, one of the ferries was allocated to this yard. The wrangle between the owner and BS dragged on and finally the owner agreed to accept the first eight ferries. Fifteen ferries in all were completed—14 by NESL and one by Appledore. The unwanted seven ferries lay in Sunderland harbour for a lengthy period before finally being sold.

This state of affairs of course had an impact on the financial outturn for the year ending March 1988. NESL recorded a loss of £51.8 million while Govan Shipbuilders recorded a loss of £28.6 million.

From the 11,000 or so employed in BS in 1985, the numbers fell to some 10,000 in 1986, to 8,600 in 1987 and to 6,600 in 1988. Of the 1988 total, the four shipbuilding companies employed between them 5,380. Clark-Kincaid, the engine builder, had reduced its labour force to some 500 because of the lack of main engine orders from the four yards—the Danish ferries provided no work in this respect.

The continuing losses being recorded by the Corporation decided the Government to dispose of the whole business. The companies were duly advertised for sale. A similar fate befell the large yard of Harland & Wolff at Belfast which had remained separate since the inception of BS back in 1977. After discussions with the European Commission, the Government announced the sale of the Belfast yard to its management, backed by Fred Olsen & Co., the Norwegian shipping company, and the sale of Govan Shipbuilders to

NORSEA — *a 31,785 gross tons ferry built for North Sea Ferries by Govan Shipbuilders in 1987.* W.S.P.L.

SUPERFLEX CHARLIE and three sister Danish ferries built by North East Shipbuilders Ltd. in Sunderland Harbour in 1989. Nigel Cutts

Kvaerner, a large Norwegian company with shipbuilding, shipping and other interests. The bombshell was then dropped— NESL was to be closed. Uproar ensued in Sunderland as M.P.s, trade unionists and employees lobbied Parliament.

Unemployment in Sunderland, already among the highest in the U.K. caused by the severe contraction of its staple industries—coal and shipbuilding—was swelled even further.

Had BS taken steps to reduce capacity from within a year of its formation and particularly during 1983, when turnover in the merchant yards fell significantly, its losses could have been mitigated. Of course, the Conservative Government returned to power in 1979 was not in favour of preserving nationalised industries. That said, much reduced losses might have persuaded it to support the companies remaining until they could be privatised.

Following these dramatic events, the remaining subsidiaries of BS were sold between December 1988 and September 1989. NESL was sold progressively in parts and this task was completed in July 1991.

Thus 1988 saw the end of the bulk of merchant shipbuilding and all of slow-running diesel engine manufacture in the U.K.

CLASSIFICATION OF SHIPYARDS

Class A

Builders of warships and when the need arose, small specialist merchant vessels. Yards in this category had to satisfy different criteria from merchant shipbuilders. The nature of the product was characterised by fairly light steel plating combined with a heavy concentration of highly complex electrical work inherent in the communications systems, weapons systems and computers. Accordingly, the composition of the labour force reflected this. Outfitting labour manhours exceeded steel trades' manhours while quality assurance had a high profile.

Because of the careful attention to detail and quality, and of course complexity, warships took years not months to build and outfit and so overheads tended to be high since they could only be recovered on a small number of vessels each year.

Yards in this category included Yarrow, Vickers-Armstrongs at Barrow, and Vosper Thornycroft.

Class B

Builders of large warships, passenger liners, ferries and, when the need arose, tankers, cargo ships, etc.

Yards in this category were all large and in addition to satisfying the criteria noted above. were equipped with extensive outfitting facilities for handling passenger ships. This required large joinery, plumbing and sheet metal departments as well as electrical. But because these yards undertook to build a variety of different types of vessel including tankers, the steelwork facilities were capable of handling heavy steelwork—thus heavy and extensive craneage was much in evidence. Overheads in these yards were very high and their recovery only possible with sufficient throughput to utilise the comprehensive facilities—a mix of warships, passenger liners, ferries and tankers, for example.

Yards in this category included Fairfield, John Brown, Beardmore, Armstrong, Whitworth (later Vickers-Armstrongs), Swan Hunter, Palmers, Cammell Laird, Harland & Wolff and Workman, Clark.

Class C

Builders of cruisers, destroyers, intermediate passenger liners, ferries, tankers and cargo liners. These yards were of medium size and able to satisfy naval requirements and able also to handle the outfitting of intermediate passenger liners. Their overheads were accordingly higher than Class D yards of around the same size.

Yards in this category included Stephen, Scotts', Swan Hunter's Neptune Yard and Hawthorn, Leslie.

Class D

Builders of high-class cargo liners, and when the need arose, all manner of other merchant vessels including tankers.

Yards in this class, wartime apart, were not engaged in naval construction nor did they build passenger ships. They were able to handle the outfitting of cargo liners of which many, up to the late 50s, carried 12 or more passengers. Such vessels were considerably more sophisticated than cargo tramps and tankers and these yards' outfitting facilities were more extensive than those of Class E yards.

Yards in this category included Harland & Wolff (Govan), Barclay, Curle, William Denny, William Hamilton, Greenock Dockyard, John Readhead, Caledon Shipbuilding, Hall, Russell and Henry Robb.

Class E

Builders of cargo tramps and tankers and very rarely other types of vessel. Frequently such vessels were built in series. In all of these yards, steelwork dominated. The numbers employed were pared to the bone as were overheads.

Yards in this category included Connell, Blythswood, Lithgows, Short Brothers, Doxford, William Pickersgill (later Austin & Pickersgill), Sir James Laing, J. L. Thompson, Bartram, Furness Shipbuilding (later Swan Hunter), Smith's Dock, Burntisland Shipbuilding, Blyth and William Gray.

CHAPTER 8

OVERVIEW OF THE DECLINE

As was noted in Chapter One, almost all Class B and C yards had their backs to the wall only once between the Wars—around 1932. In the 20s, passenger ships kept them alive but not large warships because of the Washington Naval Treaty. In the 30s, passenger ship construction continued and this work was augmented from 1935 onwards by the re-armament programme in the form of battleships, aircraft carriers, cruisers, depot ships and destroyers.

During this period, it was the Class D and E yards—particularly the latter—that took the full brunt of two depressions. Of the 184 berths sterilised by National Shipbuilders Security, all but a handful were in Class D and E yards—the exceptions being Beardmore, Workman, Clark and Palmers.

It is revealing to study the output of individual yards for 1938, just after N.S.S. had completed its work. Appendix II gives some of the details. It does not state work in progress, but confines itself to ships actually launched. Without exception, all the Class B and C yards were working to full capacity on large naval vessels in addition to the work noted in the Appendix.

A different picture emerges with the Class E yards. Laing, Short and Bartram on the River Wear, for example, were working at nowhere near full capacity. Neither was the Furness Shipbuilding Company. Once again the Class B and C yards came off best and with "cost-plus" contracts! Notwithstanding that the tramp builders had spare capacity, their importance to the industry as a whole can be gauged by the aggregate tonnage launched by these yards in 1938. In fact it was some 383,000 tons out of a total of some 1,030,000 tons for the industry, or 37%. It is probable that in terms of full capacity, Class E yards represented about 50% of the total.

Appendix III gives details of U.K. yards' order books in July 1949. Without exception every yard was busy. Naval orders had dried up, but once again the Class B and C yards came up trumps with virtually all of them featuring a passenger ship in their extensive workloads.

The Class D yards all featured cargo liners including a number with passengers. Class E yards were now at full capacity with cargo tramps and tankers. 28,000 ton deadweight tankers made their appearance.

Appendix IV gives details of U.K. yards' order books in April 1953. Once again every yard is full and Class B yards, with the sole exception of Cammell Laird, feature passenger liners in their order books. One marked difference between the composition of the workloads of 1949 and 1953 is the number of tankers on order. Once again the Class B and C yards were able to benefit. All but two vessels in Hawthorn, Leslie's order book for example comprised tankers. Even Scotts' order book was predominantly tankers. Class D and

E yards remained very busy. 44,000 ton deadweight tankers made their appearance.

The picture changes substantially by June 1959 as noted in Appendix V. At this point, most of the large yards began to increase craneage and prefabrication facilities generally in readiness for even larger tankers than the 65,000 tons deadweight ships now on order.

Class C yards' order books had also diminished.

The situation in the Class D yards had greatly deteriorated. This was entirely due to the impending demise of the cargo liner.

Class E yards remained busy with fairly substantial order books. These displayed a wide variety of foreign owners as well as home owners and they were of course now in direct competition with Continental as well as Japanese shipbuilders. This was not the case with Class B yards who all had berths big enough to construct the 65,000 ton deadweight tankers on order. No less than 40 tankers were on order in U.K. yards by the B.P. Tanker company at this time and the majority of the larger vessels were on order in Class B yards. Only 5 tankers were on order in foreign yards to B.P.'s account—all in Italy. Similar remarks apply to orders placed by Shell Tankers Ltd.

Up to 1959, the emergence of the Japanese shipbuilding industry was almost wholly confined to the construction of tankers. It is possible to say, with the benefit of hindsight, that U.K. shipbuilders had no business to assume that orders for ever-larger tankers would continue to be placed in Class B yards. They had grounds for believing this at the time since both B.P. and Shell had filled their yards with work, but it could scarcely be called competitive tendering. While the dry cargo market remained depressed in the early 60s, once again it was the Class E yards that took the brunt. The tanker market however continued to flourish but the uncompetitive prices and delays in deliveries caused more and more U.K. tanker and other owners to place orders abroad.

An event of great significance to shipbuilders across the World occurred in 1962. This was the opening of Gotaverken's Arendal shipyard in Sweden. The layout was the first among many, based upon straight-line flow of steel manufacture from stockyard to erection of block units in a shallow building dock. It brought home to U.K. shipbuilders the realisation that the schemes of modernisation already completed in all the big yards and many of the others, went only part way to embracing the latest shipbuilding technology. There was no way that most of the U.K. yards could have financed the cost of such ship factories themselves.

By the time Geddes reported in 1966, the dry cargo market had recovered, while the tanker boom continued. This did nothing however to revive the placing of orders in U.K. yards—particularly in the Class B yards.

The Suez Canal, closed in 1967 and not re-opened for 8 years, prompted tanker sizes to increase even more dramatically. Only three yards in the U.K. had the acreage available to convert into ship factories for such monster vessels. Vickers-Armstrongs in Barrow had, but had opted out of merchant shipbuilding some few years previously. Why the remaining two, Harland & Wolff and

Cammell Laird, imagined that they could, given Arendal-style facilities, compete with the Japanese for this business is hard to understand.

The Class B yards, with the notable exception of Swan Hunter, were arguably among the least competitive in the U.K. To bail them out was one thing, but to pour money in for the purposes described was ill-conceived. Had the modernisation been based upon smaller vessels, like container ships or bulk carriers for example, the resulting costs might have been less but the yards would still not have been in a position to compete with the Japanese. So we got the worst scenario of all, the wrong yards modernised and the cost of so doing maximised.

The Class E yards remaining in business after the fall-out in yards of this type in the early 60s were the ones that ought to have been supported. Austin & Pickersgill, Appledore and Sunderland Shipbuilders are good examples of continuing success following their conversion into ship factories. All three schemes were largely financed by the yards' owners, although the biggest ship that could be produced from any of them was limited to 35,000 tons deadweight.

It was certainly a tragic error on the part of many U.K. shipbuilders that they failed to design ships of the future—notably container ships and large ro-ros. While O.C.L. almost certainly did not ask U.K. yards to quote for their container ships in the mid-60s, they had little experience of Class E yards. Their passenger ships had been constructed in Class B and C yards and their cargo liners in Class D yards. Had a large ship factory been available in Sunderland and on the Lower Clyde for example, large container ships built in the U.K. might have become a reality.

The mid-60s was the "crunch point" for shipbuilding in this country. Post-Geddes, the industry, with a few notable exceptions, naval builders, Austin & Pickersgill, Appledore, Sunderland Shipbuilders and Swan Hunter, was in terminal decline.

Up to 1967 when the Shipbuilding Industry Board was formed, the U.K. shipbuilding industry was self-supporting, apart from credit terms for newbuildings— the benefit for which accrued to the shipowners, regional development grants and 2% shipbuilders relief (the percentage of the contract price per ship paid by Government).

But the losses incurred on fixed price contracts taken from 1967 onwards wiped out working capital in all but the naval builders. The S.I.B., in its disbursement of £43 million over the five year period ending in 1972, gave nothing to Doxford and Sunderland or Austin & Pickersgill (presumably because neither had merged).

This money was used largely for replacing working capital, but some was used, in the case of Swan Hunter and Scott Lithgow, for modernisation. The biggest single tranches went to Harland & Wolff (which remained separate) and U.C.S. Almost £39 million (or some 90%) of the money disbursed by the S.I.B. went to these four companies.

After 1970, when direct Government intervention took place, only a handful of companies benefited. As already noted, no less than £117 million was involved up to 1972 of which £110 million went to Cammell Laird, Harland & Wolff and Govan, all three representing sums for modernisation. In the 10 year period ending in 1977. the companies other than Cammell Laird, Harland & Wolff and Govan/U.C.S. received by way of loans and grants:

Swan Hunter	—	£ 5.8 million
Scott Lithgow	—	£ 5.2 ,,
Doxford and Sunderland	—	£ 9.0 ,,
A&P	—	£18.0 ,,
Appledore	—	£ 1.1 ,,
Yarrow	—	£ 3.4 ,,

The total involving merchant shipbuilders (i.e. excluding Yarrow) was £39 million. Set against the aid made available to the three large yards, this was bizarre!

Doxford and Sunderland's three shipyards on the Wear had traditionally built tramps and oil tankers. Austin & Pickersgill nearby had traditionally built tramps. Their culture was similar—highly competitive, low overheads and with a wide range of U.K. and foreign clients. All four yards were modernised and thereafter built the successors to the tramp and the 12,000 ton deadweight tanker—namely S.D.14s, tankers and bulk carriers of up to 150,000 tons deadweight. They were able to maintain a reasonable workload throughout the 60s and into the 70s.

Lithgows and Connells on the Clyde were in a similar category. But none of these four companies, with the possible exception of Lithgows, had the design staff nor the outfitting facilities to tackle the more sophisticated types of ships that were emerging at this time like containerships and large ro-ros.

Cammell Laird and Harland & Wolff were two yards that had the design clout and the yard facilities to build for the sophisticated end of the market. Instead they stuck to tankers and bulk carriers and as a result and despite their newly Government-funded facilities were up against the fiercest of all foreign competition.

Swan Hunter was the only company which combined series building of tankers and bulkers of various sizes with the sophisticated end of the market.

Nationalisation was the last straw. Although industrial disputes became rarer, this change came too late to save the industry. In any case, productivity continued to fall while wages soared under the influence of the Fair Wages Act. Moreover morale among the workforce, management included, became lower and lower as wave after wave of redundancies was implemented, followed by company closures. Management were dismayed at the continuing losses and felt impotent to halt the decline.

The fact that a nationalised industry cannot go bankrupt led some shipowners to adopt a somewhat cavalier attitude towards the clauses in shipbuilding contracts. Prior to nationalisation, a shipowner knew that pushing a shipbuilder too far in relation to the interpretation of the specification, leading to additional costs for what were in effect extras, could easily force the shipbuilder into receivership. In this event, the shipowner would be left with an unfinished ship for which he had already paid some of the instalments. The market collapse of 1975, followed by nationalisation, prompted some shipowners to refuse to accept ships on grounds not wholly consistent with the contract terms. Such actions led to a large escalation of losses.

It is revealing to compare the individual merchant yards' financial performance over the 10 year life of British Shipbuilders. Table 2 gives the details and from this table can be the seen the year in which a number of the yards were either closed or sold to the private sector.

The most significant feature of Table 2 is the consistency of losses by all companies. It has to be remembered, of course, that merchant work was very difficult to obtain following the market collapse in 1975 and the emergence of South Korea as a world force in shipbuilding. Thus the pure merchant shipbuilders suffered work shortages throughout the period. Govan Shipbuilders returned consistently bad figures.

The yards that constructed naval as well as merchant ships—namely Cammell Laird and Swan Hunter—fared no better than the pure merchant yards, despite their profitable warship element.

Easily the worst financial performance was that of Scott Lithgow who, during the period, built supertankers and offshore structures but despite the inclusion of some naval work in their workload, returned huge losses.

Table 3 details the turnover of the yards from 1981 to 1988. The figures for Austin & Pickersgill and Govan bear a striking similarity. The former registered a turnover of some £61 million in 1983. In the three subsequent years this had fallen to less than half that figure. Similar remarks apply to Govan. While the extent to which a reduction in the labour force reflects the loss in turnover, such a reduction has no effect on fixed overheads. In short— there was too much capacity. In the case of Austin & Pickersgill, the reason was not hard to find. The last S.D.14 was completed in 1984. This highly successful standard ship had run its course with an immediate impact on sales.

Cammell Laird and Scott Lithgow exhibited large fluctuations in turnover, indicative of under-recovered overheads in those years when sales were low. The remaining yards demonstrated a certain consistency in turnover but this does not necessarily indicate that they were utilising their full capacity.

The figures for 1984 surely pointed to the need for a reduction in capacity, given that the shipping market remained at a low ebb. One or more of the yards listed should have been either closed at this point or, preferably, an attempt made to sell them to the private sector, thus hopefully trying to preserve a measure of employment.

Had the industry not been nationalised, the yards on the North East coast could have been supported by Government at comparatively modest cost. But the industry was nationalised and very ironically, by the time B.S. was wound up in 1989, all that remained of Merchant Shipbuilding, apart from Appledore and a slimmed-down Swan Hunter, was Cammell Laird, Harland & Wolff and Govan!

TABLE 2
Merchant Yards—Trading Profits (Losses)—£000s

	Appledore	A&P	Cammell Laird	Govan	Robb Caledon
1978	(3,469)	(158)	(28,056)	(10,525)	(7,541)
1979	(130)	802	8,497	(14,879)	(3,365)
1980	(2,132)	(6,365)	(3,552)	(14,920)	(5,720)
1981	(1,646)	(11,542)	(6,547)	(12,980)	(2,151)
1982	(356)	(8,949)	242	(6,287)	(4,427)
1983	(127)	414	(12,632)	(12,475)	—
1984	(4,376)	(19,710)	(23,786)	(12,846)	—
1985	(7,350)	(8,032)	(5,207)	(18,349)	—
1986	(5,588)	(16,574)	—	(13,921)	—
1987	(7,342)	—	—	(31,389)	—
1988	(13,404)	—	—	(28,618)	—
TOTALS	(45,920)	(70,114)	(71,041)	(177,189)	(23,204)

	Scott Lithgow	Smith's Dock	Sunderland Shipbuilders	Swan Hunter	NESL
1978	(22,497)	(6,141)	(2,192)	(11,295)	—
1979	(7,073)	(5,225)	(2,744)	(14,253)	—
1980	(31,671)	(9,946)	(19,321)	(15,702)	—
1981	(14,444)	(6,058)	(624)	1,831	—
1982	(14,949)	(2,202)	(5,605)	83	—
1983	(65,982)	106	(1,806)	(38,006)	—
1984	(74,584)	(1,180)	(12,657)	(7,392)	—
1985	—	(11,025)	4,874	13,380	—
1986	—	(9,382)	(18,947)	—	—
1987	—	(720)	—	—	(56,031)
1988	—	—	—	—	(51,830)
TOTALS	(231,200)	(51,773)	(68,770)	(71,354)	(107,861)

TABLE 3
Turnover (£000s)

	1981	1982	1983	1984	1985	1986	1987	1988
A&P	50,376	65,457	61,350	27,148	21,984	25,261	—	—
Govan	40,683	52,630	67,514	32,828	30,140	36,613	22,135	35,301
Smith's Dock	26,763	30,688	38,720	25,623	22,824	29,814	14,526	—
Sunderland	55,772	59,323	58,554	50,108	52,172	52,122	—	—
Appledore	21,395	14,604	20,768	24,421	14,720	11,910	—	—
Swan Hunter	124,568	120,874	110,972	102,406	137,136	—	—	—
Cammell Laird	28,850	52,722	65,890	45,782	21,371	—	—	—
NESL	—	—	—	—	—	—	68,717	74,601
Scott Lithgow	65,594	74,735	105,548	40,844	—	—	—	—

CHAPTER 9

POSTSCRIPT

There can be no managers in industry who would welcome political interference in their business. Shipbuilders were no exception. Business should stand or fall by its own efforts and market forces are one important factor of the outcome. But when the world market in shipbuilding is so distorted by overcapacity and by Government subsidy, a single company's efforts to survive, let alone prosper, are rendered impotent.

In such circumstances, only Government can make financial assistance available since private capital would not be forthcoming as against the risks involved. In the case of the U.K. shipbuilding industry, the Labour Government under James Callaghan was committed to a policy of nationalisation. Had a Conservative Government been in power at the time, nationalisation of the industry would probably not have occurred. Since many of the individual shipbuilding companies were all but bankrupt at this point, any action which a Tory government took would have had to be swift if large scale unemployment was not to result.

Assuming that a Tory government had been prepared to make public funds available, whether or not it preserved every shipbuilding company trading at that point, it would have made no difference in the long run to the policy adopted. Irrespective of party, whether nationalised or not. when governments make public funds available to an industry, there is a heavy price to pay.

Governments rightly consider that they have a duty to account for public spending and while this is not denied, it is the methods by which this duty is achieved that stultifies the entrepreneurial spirit. It appears that for state owned/state assisted companies, governments of any party require:
1) The formation of a Board of Directors appointed by them.
2) The imposition of a statutory duty on that Board to produce a 5 year rolling Corporate Plan.
3) The creation of layers of civil servants whose duties are to monitor the financial and employment outcomes of the Plan.

The lines of communication are thus established—the appointed Board Members parley with the civil servants concerned and frequently neither have experience of the particular industry. The net result is that the industry that Government is attempting to assist seldom has its case properly presented. The relevant parties—Government ministers and industrial managers—seldom meet.

Government intervention in shipbuilding over the years has been disastrous. Between the Wars it was "too little — too late". In the early 60s, save for the introduction of credit for shipowners, it did nothing to halt yard closures. In the late 60s and early 70s, it was a case of "too much — too late" — and to the wrong companies. In the late 70s, it was "too much — regardless". In the early 80s, it was "hard and relentless".

Although the Government had decided to withdraw its support for U.K. merchant shipbuilding, namely British Shipbuilders, long before it actually happened, the closure of NESL on the River Wear marked the end, in all but name, of the Corporation. Government has never actually confirmed that the closure of NESL was part of a deal struck with the European Commission under which Harland & Wolff and Govan would be privatised. There can be little doubt that this is what transpired and in the process, the huge accumulated debts of both companies were presumably written off while allowing the purchasers bargain prices. NESL was given but two years of existence in the worst possible shipping market before it was unceremoniously axed. Two of the finest shipbuilding facilities in Europe were denied any future in shipbuilding.

In 1993, we learnt that Swan Hunter, privatised in 1986 by way of a management buy-out, was fast running out of naval work. The terms of the buy-out incorporated a provision that no intervention fund subsidy would be granted by Government to the company thus effectively preventing it from building merchant ships. In 1986 this condition attached to the buy-out was acceptable to the purchasers. The requirements of the armed forces have radically altered since then with the end of the Cold War and the latest Government Defence Review White Paper has detailed a significant reduction in surface vessels for the Royal Navy. This must in turn impact upon the future size of the Royal Fleet Auxiliary. Swan Hunter had been for many years involved with both and it is not too much to say was the country's leading builder of R.F.As.

With outfitting work well advanced on three Type 23 frigates and with no work to follow and with steelworking facilities idle, Swan Hunter faced closure unless they could win the contract for a helicopter carrier. They faced competition only from Vickers, since neither Yarrow nor Vospers had berths large enough to accommodate the subject vessel. In the knowledge that Swan Hunter's failure to secure this one vessel would almost certainly result in closure, Government, apparently on grounds of cost, still awarded the contract to Vickers.

It is difficult to believe that Vickers' stated tender price was £71 million less than that of Swan Hunter. The fact that the construction of the hull was sub-contracted to Kvaerner Govan does not necessarily alter this view, because it is submitted that Swan Hunter was quite capable of building the hull as cheaply as Kvaerner Govan.

What is clear is that Swan Hunter, a privatised company, was in no position to tender at a loss. Vickers may have chosen to submit a loss-making tender for the purpose of trying to secure a monopoly of future orders for large surface warships, as well as for nuclear submarines. Government, for its part, presumably was satisfied that both companies tendered on precisely the same basis.

The Receiver was called in to Swan Hunter days after the contract was awarded to Vickers. Shortly afterwards, we are told, Government tried unsuccessfully to persuade the European Commission to reverse their decision made in 1986 not to allow Swan Hunter Intervention Fund subsidy. In spite of the radically altered naval requirements and the desperate plight of Swan Hunter, the Commission refused. Government meanwhile permitted the yard to complete the three frigates while the Receiver was endeavouring to find a buyer for the business. Who wants a shipyard confined by a strait-jacket?

In 1994, in a belated effort to bring some relief, Government persuaded the European Commission to allow a modest amount of Intervention Fund subsidy which would, in theory, permit the yard to tender for a few merchant ships. Meanwhile work was rapidly running out as each frigate was completed and the Receiver had no option but to declare more and more redundancies.

A buyer for the yard appeared from France and eventually made an offer to purchase, subject to the Ministry of Defence awarding the yard the contract for the refit of a Royal Fleet Auxiliary. Hope rose on the Tyne, only to be dashed when the refit was awarded elsewhere. It would have been a small price to pay for the prospect of the yard remaining open albeit on a small scale. The potential buyer bowed out.

Around the time of delivery of the last frigate, another buyer appeared but regrettably could not satisfy the Receiver as to his financial backing and it looked inevitable that the assets of the yard were now to be sold.

An auction of the shipyard plant and equipment was arranged by the Receivers to take place on 20th June 1995, but only seven days before this event, Swan Hunter was rescued.

The Hartlepool-based T.H.C. Group (an offshore fabricator) offered to purchase the yard, Tyne & Wear Development Corporation pledging £500,000 towards the project. The Receivers accepted the offer. The new owners expect to create 600 jobs and have named the company Swan Hunter (Tyneside) Ltd.

One of the Swan Hunter "Save our Shipyard" campaigners put the matter into sharp focus when he remarked, "T.H.C. have seen the business opportunity on offer at Swan's which was so sadly missed by the Government".

More recently, the Ministry of Defence has announced an invitation to tender for two fleet oilers for the Royal Fleet Auxiliary to replace two existing vessels constructed in the 60s. It was reported that feasibility studies had been undertaken into this question as early as 1994. These apparently were concluded early in 1995, some months before the "funeral" of Swan Hunter in June of that year.

In November 1995, the naval procurement programme was stated to be:
new air defence frigates
a helicopter carrier (already launched)
up to two assault ships
three Type 23 frigates
two fleet oilers (noted above)
up to five Batch 2 Trafalgar class submarines
together with a number of minehunters and survey vessels.

While this substantial programme may be spread over a number of years, it was surely illogical to exclude Swan Hunter—the prime builder of R.F.A. vessels—from any involvement with this work. The argument in short is, not that Government should have "saved" Swan Hunter, but rather that they should have preserved real competition.

In July 1993 a report was published by the Norwegian ECON Analysis Institute indicating that European yards were providing "subsidies hidden through state-involvement in yards in which national coffers covered company deficits". It quoted two examples of this. Howaldtswerke-Deutsche Werft of Kiel offered a price of $90 million for the world's largest container ships, while admitting eight months previously to the Commission that the ships would cost $140 million to produce. The other case concerned Fincantieri of Italy who apparently "received one billion pounds from the state holding company I.R.I. between 1987 and 1991 in transfers that were not included in EC-designated ceiling subsidy payments to yards". ECON went on to quote the value of subsidies paid as a percentage of contract value in other shipbuilding countries, as follows:

COUNTRY	%
Italy	15 to 50
France	12 to 15
Germany	23 to 35
Spain	15 to 30
Norway	12
Denmark	8 to 13
Holland	9 to 12
Britain	9 to 12
Finland	3 to 5
Japan	3 to 5
South Korea	3 to 5

In late 1994, British Aerospace made a bid to take over Vickers. A few days later it was revealed that G.E.C. (owner of Yarrow) had made a higher bid. BAe tried to persuade the Ministry of Defence that a take-over by G.E.C. would create a monopoly situation insofar as large surface warships were concerned, while G.E.C. denied this.

With Swan Hunter and Harland & Wolff presumably no longer constructing large warships or Royal Fleet Auxiliary ships, the field is left wide open for Vickers and Yarrow to build these. If Yarrow has facilities large enough to construct the replacements for the two ageing assault ships and R.F.As, then combining them into one company does create a monopoly situation. If Yarrow's facilities are not large enough it still makes sense, so far as G.E.C. is concerned, for they would then own the yard that has already created a monopoly in large surface warships. Either way, for future tendering for nuclear submarines, large surface warships and R.F.As, Government seem quite content for only one firm to be involved.

In 1995 it was announced that G.E.C. had won the take-over battle. The new owners confirmed their intention to keep the Yarrow yard open.

BIBLIOGRAPHY

Hogwood — Government and Shipbuilding — The Politics of Industrial Change

Booz Allen Report

Geddes Report

Cammell Laird—The Golden Years

Shipbuilders to the World (125 Years of Harland & Wolff)—Moss & Hume

James Lithgow—Master of Work—J. Reid

Song of the Clyde—Fred Walker

Economic Decline in Britain — The Shipbuilding Industry 1890/1970—E. Lorenz.

The Decline of British Shipbuilding Since the Second World War—P. Hilditch

New History of British Shipping—R. Hope

Brassey's Naval Annual—1938

Glasgow Herald Trade Review—1938

Where Ships are Born—Wear Shipbuilders Association—1953

History of North East Shipbuilding—D. Dougan

Steel and Ships—Sir Alan Grant

New Construction in Hand or on Order (New Series — Nos. 16, and 31)— Journal of Commerce and Shipping Telegraph

Merchant Ships under Construction and on Order (June 1959—Shipping World and World Shipbuilding)

APPENDIX I

Progress photographs showing the building in 1941 of Caledon Yard No. 393, EMPIRE HEYWOOD.

The keel is laid, 21st June 1941

25th June 1941.

2nd July 1941.

9th July 1941.

97

16th July 1941.

23rd July 1941.

6th August 1941.

23rd July 1941.

30th July 1941.

6th August 1941.

14th August 1941.

14th August 1941.

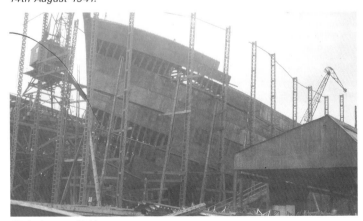

20th August 1941.

100

27th August 1941.

3rd September 1941.

10th September 1941.

101

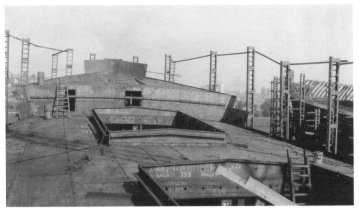

17th September 1941.

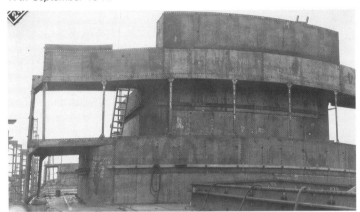

24th September 1941.

1st October 1941.

Launch day, 21st October 1941

APPENDIX II

Extracts from "The Glasgow Herald Trade Review", 29th December 1938 showing ships launched by major British yards during the year.

Name	Flag	Type	Tonnage
Barclay, Curle & Co. Ltd., Glasgow			
Etrrick	Br	m.pass./cargo	11,279
Orna	Br	m.cargo	6,779
Bulolo	Au	m.pass./cargo	6,267
Bartram & Sons Ltd., Sunderland			
Lodestone	Br	s.cargo	4,877
Suva	Au	s.cargo	4,873
Agios Georgios IV	Gr	s.cargo	4,847
Blyth Dry Docks & Shipbuilding Co. Ltd., Blyth			
Barbican	Br	R.N. boom	690
Barbrook	Br	defence	690
Barcastle	Br	vessels	690
Bayonet	Br	R.N. boom	530
Falconet	Br	working vessels	530
Blythswood Shipbuilding Co. Ltd., Scotstoun			
Kars	Br	m.tanker	9,100
San Demetrio	Br	m.tanker	8,074
Manchester Progress	Br	s.cargo	5,621
Scottish Prince	Br	m.cargo	4,917
Rafaela	Ne	s.tanker	3,177
Ordolina	Bz	tank barge	260
John Brown & Co. Ltd., Clydebank			
Queen Elizabeth	Br	Express liner	85,000
Forth	Br	R.N. depot ship	11,700
Jackal	Br	R.N. destroyer	1,690
Javelin	Br	R.N. destroyer	1,690
(all steam turbine propelled)			
Burntisland Shipbuilding Co. Ltd., Burntisland			
Derrynane	Br	s.cargo	4,896
Aspasia Nomikos	Gr	s.cargo	4,855
Derrymore	Br	m.cargo	4,799
Gran	No	m.cargo/pass.	4,140
Robur VIII	Pol	s.cargo	2,864
Matthew Flinders	Au	s.cargo	2,235
Fulham IV	Br	s.cargo	1,584
Portsea	Br	s.cargo	1,583
Caledon Shipbuilding & Engineering Co. Ltd., Dundee			
Glenearn	Br	m.cargo/pass.	8,986
Scottish Monarch	Br	s.cargo	4,718
Beaconsfield	Br	s.cargo	4,635
Barossa	Au	s.cargo	4,239
Seaforth	Br	m.cargo	4,124
Tambua	Au	s.molasses/cargo	3,566
Scott	Br	R.N. sloop	840
Cammell Laird & Co. Ltd., Birkenhead			
Mauretania	Br	s.passenger	34,000
British Sincerity	Br	m.tanker	8,402
City of Edinburgh	Br	s.cargo	8,046
City of Lincoln	Br	s.cargo	8,046
Jonathan Holt	Br	s.cargo	3,881
John Holt	Br	s.cargo	3,881
Thetis	Br	R.N. submarine	1,100
Trident	Br	R.N. submarine	1,100

Name	Flag	Type	Tonnage
Charles Connell & Co. Ltd., Scotstoun			
Mountpark	Br	s.cargo	4,648
Wellpark	Br	s.cargo	4,649
Rothermere	Br	s.cargo	5,350
Baron Semple	Br	s.cargo	4,766
William Denny & Bros. Ltd., Dumbarton			
Kindat	Br	s.cargo	4,358
Katha	Br	s.cargo	4,357
Jaguar	Br	R.N. destroyer	1,690
Auckland	Br	R.N. sloop	1,200
Oron	Br	m.ferry	277
Lymington	Br	m.ferry	275
Rona	Br	fishery patrol	180
William Doxford & Sons Ltd., Sunderland			
British Genius	Br	m.tanker	8,547
Themoni	Gr	s.cargo	5,719
Starstone	Br	s.cargo	5,702
Lady Glanely	Br	m.cargo	5,497
Nonsuco	U.S.	m.cargo	5,219
Ittersum	Ne	s.cargo	5,199
S. Thome	Po	m.cargo	5,179
Clifton Hall	Br	m.cargo	5,062
Willowbank	Br	m.cargo	5,029
Fairfield Shipbuilding & Engineering Co. Ltd., Govan			
Devonshire	Br	m.passenger	11,300
Juno	Br	R.N. destroyer	1,690
Furness Shipbuilding Co. Ltd., Haverton Hill-on-Tees			
British Liberty	Br	m.tanker	8,300
San Delfino	Br	m.tanker	8,072
San Ernesto	Br	m.tanker	8,072
Tasajera	Br	s.tanker	3,952
Rosalia	Ne	s.tanker	3,177
Rebeca	Ne	s.tanker	3,176
William Gray & Co. Ltd., West Hartlepool			
Indora	Br	s.cargo	6,622
Chios	Gr	s.cargo	5,650
George M. Livanos	Gr	s.cargo	5,482
Michael Livanos	Gr	s.cargo	4,774
Mary Livanos	Gr	s.cargo	4,772
Fauzon	Fr	s.cargo	4,376
Arijon	Fr	s.cargo	4,374
Corinthian	Br	s.cargo	3,122
Ionian	Br	s.cargo	3,114
Palermo	Br	s.cargo	2,928
Tintern Abbey	Br	s.cargo	2,471
Greenock Dockyard Co. Ltd., Greenock			
Clan Forbes	Br	s.cargo	7,529
Clan Fraser	Br	s.cargo	7,529
Clan Ferguson	Br	s.cargo	7,347
Clan Menzies	Br	s.cargo	7,336

William Hamilton & Co. Ltd., Port Glasgow

Malabar	Br	s.cargo	7,975
Wray Castle	Br	s.cargo	4,253
Mount Ida	Br	s.cargo	4,202
Speedy	Br	R.N. minesweeper	875

Harland Wolff Ltd., Belfast

Durban Castle	Br	m.pass/cargo	17,388
Pretoria Castle	Br	m.pass/cargo	17,388
Waimarama	Br	m.pass/cargo	11,092
Belfast	Br	R.N. cruiser	10,000
Erato	Br	m.tanker	8,000
Richmond Castle	Br	m.cargo	7,800
Rowallan Castle	Br	m.cargo	7,800

Harland & Wolff Ltd., Govan

Lochavon	Br	m.cargo	9,205
British Fidelity	Br	m.tanker	8,465
British Trust	Br	m.tanker	8,465
Donax	Br	m.tanker	8,036
Dromus	Br	m.tanker	8,036
San Emiliano	Br	m.tanker	8,000

R. & W. Hawthorn, Leslie & Co. Ltd., Hebburn

Daronia	Br	m.tanker	8,170
Daphnella	Br	m.tanker	8,078
Doryssa	Br	m.tanker	8,078
Waipori	Br	s.cargo	4,282
Cycle	Br	s.cargo	4,000
Jervis	Br	R.N. destroyer	1,650
Kelly	Br	R.N. destroyer	1,650

Sir James Laing & Sons Ltd., Sunderland

Eidanger	No	m.tanker	9,432
Alar	No	m.tanker	9,432
Grayburn	Br	s.cargo	6,342
Aelybryn	Br	s.cargo	4,985

Lithgows Ltd., Port Glasgow

British Unity	Br	m.tanker	8,570
Davila	Br	m.tanker	8,054
Dorcasia	Br	m.tanker	8,054
Dosinia	Br	m.tanker	8,054
San Eliseo	Br	m.tanker	8,020
Triadic	Br	m.cargo	6,378
Scientist	Br	s.cargo	6,199
El Hind	In	s.pilgrim ship	5,319
—	Br	s.cargo	5,200
Coultarn	Br	s.cargo	3,759

Wm. Pickersgill & Sons Ltd., Sunderland

Goodleigh	Br	s.cargo	5,448
Egton	Br	s.cargo	4,363

John Readhead & Sons Ltd., South Shields

Turkistan	Br	s.cargo	6,960
Shahristan	Br	s.cargo	6,935
Sutherland	Br	s.cargo	5,083

Scott's Shipbuilding & Engineering Co. Ltd., Greenock

Glenroy	Br	m.cargo	9,700
Tribune	Br	R.N. submarine	1,095

Short Brothers Ltd., Sunderland

Elias G. Kulukundis	Gr	s.cargo	5,549
Helene Kulukundis	Gr	s.cargo	5,548
Master Elias Kulukundis	Gr	s.cargo	5,548

Smith's Dock Co. Ltd., South Bank-on-Tees

Capitaine Saint Martin	Fr	s.cargo	3,450
Cerion	Br	m.cargo	2,588
No. 1037	—	s.cargo	1,930
Avila	Br	s.tanker	1,635
Magnet	Br	} R.N. boom	550
Martinet	Br	} working vessels	550
Ayrshire	Br	s.trawler	540
Fifeshire	Br	s.trawler	540
Argyllshire	Br	s.trawler	540
Imperialist	Br	s.trawler	540
Bembridge	Br	s.pilot vessel	413

Alexander Stephen & Sons Ltd., Linthouse

Canton	Br	s.passenger	15,784
Surat	Br	m.cargo	5,529
Shillong	Br	m.cargo	5,529
Komata	NZ	s.cargo	3,900
Kurow	NZ	s.cargo	3,900
Korowai	NZ	s.cargo	2,525

Swan, Hunter & Wigham Richardson Ltd. Wallsend and Neptune Yards

Dominion Monarch	Br	m.pass./cargo	26,470
Sobieski	Pol	m.pass./cargo	10,800
Regent Tiger	Br	m.tanker	10,180
Edinburgh	Br	R.N. cruiser	10,000
British Tenacity	Br	m.tanker	8,460
Amra	Br	s.pass./cargo	8,314
Umgeni	Br	s.pass./cargo	8,180
La Carriere	Br	s.tanker	5,690
Hopepeak	Br	m.cargo	5,180
Janus	Br	R.N. destroyer	1,690
Volo	Br	s.cargo	1,587
Lida	Pol	s.cargo	1,387

Joseph L. Thompson & Sons Ltd., Sunderland

Sandanger	No	m.tanker	9,432
Silverlaurel	Br	s.cargo	6,100
Sire	Br	s.cargo	5,664
Lerwick	Br	s.cargo	5,626
Welsh Trader	Br	s.cargo	4,974
St. Elwyn	Br	s.cargo	4,940
Scottish Trader	Br	s.cargo	4,016

Vickers-Armstrongs Ltd., Barrow-in-Furness

Triumph	Br	R.N. submarine	1,095
Thistle	Br	R.N. submarine	1,095
Ursula	Br	R.N. submarine	540
Unity	Br	R.N. submarine	540
Swan	Br	m.passenger	250

Key: Au: Australian, Br: British, Bz: Brazilian, Fr: French, Gr: Greek, In: Indian, Ne: Dutch, No: Norwegian, Pol: Polish, Po: Portuguese, U.S.: United States.

APPENDIX III

Extracts from the July 1949 edition of "New Construction in Hand or on Order" — Merchant Shipbuilding in British yards.

Barclay, Curle & Co. Ltd., Whiteinch, Glasgow

P.&O. S.N. Co. Ltd.	9,700d	Cargo
British India S.N. Co. Ltd.	10,550d	Refrig. cargo
British India S.N. Co. Ltd.	7,500g	Cargo
British India S.N. Co. Ltd.	10,000g	Cargo and pass.
British India S.N. Co. Ltd. (two ships	15,000g	Pass. and Cargo
Melsom & Melsom, Larvik (two ships)	13,000g	Tanker
British India S.N. Co. Ltd. (two ships)	9,000g	Cargo
British India S.N. Co. Ltd.	5,200g	Cargo and pass.

Bartram & Sons Ltd., South Dock, Sunderland

A. P. Moller, Copenhagen (two ships)	5,700g	Cargo
Companhia Nacional de Navegacao, Lisbon	6,100g	Cargo and pass.
Phs. Van Ommeren's Shipping Co., Rotterdam	10,450d	Cargo
Gdynia-America Shipping Lines Ltd. (two ships)	7,600g	Tankers
Royal Interoceaan Lines, Amsterdam	8,800d	Cargo

Blyth Dry Docks and Shipbuilding Co. Ltd., Blyth

Cia. de Navegacao Carregadores Acoreanos, Azores	2,700g	Cargo
Lancashire Shipping Co. Ltd. (two ships)	8,650g	Cargo and pass.
A. P. Moller, Copenhagen (two ships)	12,600d	Tankers
Skibs. A/B Vilhelm Torkildsens Rederi, Bergen (two ships)	3,500d	Cargo
Elder Dempster Lines Ltd.	1,500d	Coaster
Polish British Steamship Co.	2,900d	Refrig. cargo

Blythswood Shipbuilding Co. Ltd., Scotstoun

Bruusgaard Kiosterud & Co. Ltd., Drammen	10,500g	Tanker
C. T. Bowing & Co. Ltd.	8,300g	Tanker
Hvalfslsk. Globus A/S, Nanset	11,500g	Tanker
Medomsley Steam Shipping Co. Ltd.	6,870g	Cargo and pass.
Manchester Liners Ltd.	5,900g	Cargo and pass.
British Tanker Co. Ltd.	8,500g	Tanker
Skibs. A/S William Hansens Rederi, Bergen	2,480g	Tanker
C. T. Bowring & Co. Ltd. (two ships)	11,500g	Tankers

John Brown & Co. Ltd., Clydebank

New Zealand Shipping Co. Ltd.	19,000g	Pass. and cargo
Tanker Corporation, Panama (two ships)	18,000d	Tankers

Federal Steam Navigation Co. Ltd.	8,500g	Cargo
Maritime Trading Ltd., Panama (two ships)	19,000d	Tankers
Blue Star Line	13,000g	Cargo
New Zealand Shipping Co. Ltd.	14,000g	Pass. and cargo
British Railway Executive	5,000g	Passenger
P.&O. S.N. Co. Ltd.	9,000g	Cargo and pass.
British Railway Executive	3,150g	Train ferry

Burntisland Shipbuilding Co. Ltd., Burntisland

A/S Inger (Jacob Kjode, A/S) Bergen	4,350g	Cargo liner
E. B. Aaby's Rederi A/S, Oslo (two ships)	4,830g	Cargo liners
Van Nievelt, Goudriaan & Co.'s Stoomvaart Mij., Rotterdam	4,700g	Cargo liner
Prince Line Ltd. (Furness Withy & Co. Ltd., managers)	2,360g	liner
Prince Line Ltd. (Furness Withy & Co. Ltd., managers) (two ships)	3,200g	Cargo liners
Johnston Warren Lines Ltd. (Furness Withy & Co. Ltd., managers)	3,200g	Cargo liner
Stephenson Clarke Ltd.	2,925g	Collier
Stephenson Clarke Ltd.	1,470g	Collier
Wood Lines Ltd.	1,650g	Cargo liner
Stanhope Steamship Co. Ltd.	5,500g	Cargo
McCowen & Gross Ltd.	5,600g	Cargo
South Eastern Gas Board	1,890g	Up-river collier
Scheepvaart en Steenkolen Mij. N.V., Rotterdam	2,750g	Collier
Shipping and Coal Co. Ltd., London	2,750g	Collier

Caledon Shipbuilding & Engineering Co. Ltd., Dundee

Britain Steamship Co. Ltd. (Watts, Watts & Co. Ltd., managers) (three ships)	8,000d	Cargo
Currie Line Ltd.	3,600d	Cargo
Alfred Holt & Company	9,000d	Pass. and cargo
Olof Wallenius, Stockholm	13,500d	Tanker
Clyde Shipping Co. Ltd., (two ships)	1,100d	Cargo
North of Scotland and Orkney and Shetland Steam Navigation Co. Ltd.	735d	Cargo and pass.
Iver Bugge, Larvik	13,500d	Tanker
Moss Hutchison Line	4,000d	Cargo and pass.
N.V. Stoomvaart Mij. Nederland, Amsterdam	10,000d	Cargo
Dundee Harbour Trustees	450g	Ferry

Cammell Laird & Co. Ltd., Birkenhead

Alfred Holt & Company	10,250g	Cargo
British & Continental Steamship Co., Ltd.	2,500g	Cargo
Ellerman Lines Ltd.	7,000g	Cargo
Argentine Government (two ships)	7,500g	Cargo and pass.
British Tanker Co. Ltd. (two ships)	8,450g	Tankers
Anglo-Saxon Petroleum Co. Ltd.	28,000d	Tanker
Shaw Savill & Albion Co. Ltd.	13,000g	Refrig. cargo
Argentine Government (four ships)	18,400d	Tankers
Blue Star Line	13,000g	Refrig. cargo
British Tanker Co.	28,000d	Tanker
Isle of Man S.P. Co. Ltd.	2,500g	Passenger
Ellerman Lines Ltd.	11,000g	Cargo

Charles Connell & Co. Ltd., Scotstoun

Ben Line Steamers	8,000g	Cargo
H. M. Wrangell A/S, Haugesund	9,000d	Cargo
Wilh. Wilhelmsen, Oslo	10,300d	Cargo
Wilh. Wilhelmsen, Oslo	16,000d	Tanker
Jacob Kjode A/S, Bergen	16,000d	Tanker
Bergenske D/S, Bergen	16,000d	Tanker
James Nourse Ltd. (two ships)	9,000g	Cargo
Denholm Line Steamers Ltd.	9,600g	Cargo

William Denny & Bros. Ltd., Dumbarton

William Denny & Bros. Ltd.	230g	Double-ended paddle ferry
Railway Executive Southern Region	2,400g	Passenger
Ellerman Lines Ltd.	7,000g	Cargo
Ellerman Lines Ltd.	10,000g	Cargo
Indo-China Steam Navigation Co. Ltd.	7,800g	Pass. and cargo
British India Steam Navigation Co. Ltd. (two ships)	5,420g	Cargo
Burns and Laird Lines Ltd.	850g	Cattle and cargo
British & Burmese Steam Navigation Co. Ltd.	5,600g	Cargo
Union Steam Ship Co. of New Zealand Ltd.	5,100g	Pass. and cargo
Corporation of Wallasey	700g	Passenger ferry
Railway Executive, Southern Region	837g	Passenger ferry

Sundry small craft for shipment abroad.

William Doxford & Sons Ltd., Pallion, Sunderland

British Tanker Co. Ltd.	8,640g	Tanker
British Tanker Co. Ltd. (two ships)	6,160g	Tankers
Hain Steamship Co Ltd. (four ships)	5,300g	Cargo
Buries Markes Ltd.	6,330g	Cargo and pass.
British Tanker Co. Ltd. (two ships)	8,700g	Tankers
Moor Line Ltd. (two ships)	5,300g	Cargo

Overseas Tankship Corporation, New York (four ships)	8,600g	Tankers
Reardon Smith & Sons Ltd. (two ships)	5,500g	Cargo
West Hartlepool Steam Navigation Co. Ltd.	5,500g	Cargo
Thos. and Jas. Harrison (two ships)	8,100g	Cargo

Fairfield Shipbuilding & Engineering Co. Ltd., Govan

Bibby Line	9,200g	Pass. and cargo
Blue Star Line (two ships)	11,000d	Pass. and cargo
British Tanker Co.	28,000d	Tanker
Canadian Pacific Railways	6,000g	Pass. and car ferry

Furness Shipbuilding Co. Ltd., Haverton Hill-on-Tees

Eagle Oil & Shipping Co. Ltd.	15,000d	Tanker
Ellerman Lines Ltd.	10,800d	Cargo
Erling H. Samuelsen, Oslo	24,500d	Tanker
Fearnley & Eger, Oslo	24,500d	Tanker
Anders Jahre, Sandefjord	24,500d	Tanker
S. Ugelstads Rederi A/S, Oslo	24,500d	Tanker
H. M. Wrangell & Co., A/S, Haugesund	24,500d	Tanker
Counties Ship Management Co. Ltd. (two ships)	16,300d	Tankers
H. Ditlev-Simonsen & Co., Oslo	24,500d	Tanker
Knut Knutsen O.A.S., Haugesund	24,500d	Tanker
British Tanker Co. Ltd. (two ships)	12,250d	Tankers
E. Hogberg, Stockholm (two ships)	16,300d	Tankers
American owners (two ships)	24,500d	Tankers
Overseas Tankship Corporation, New York	16,500d	Tanker
Hunting & Son Ltd. (two ships)	16,300d	Tankers
Eagle Oil & Shipping Co. Ltd. (two ships)	15,000d	Tankers
Tschudi & Eitzen, Oslo	24,500d	Tanker

William Gray & Co. Ltd., West Hartlepool

Maritime Shipping and Trading Co. Ltd.	8,800d	Cargo
Dannebrog S/S Co, Copenhagen	3,400d	Cargo
S. G. Livanos, Piraeus	12,000d	Cargo
Irish Shipping Ltd. (two ships)	9,000d	Cargo
Dannebrog S/S Co.	3,400d	Cargo
D/S A/S Progress, Copenhagen	3,400d	Cargo
Van Nievelt, Goudriaan, Rotterdam (hull only)	9,200d	Cargo
S. G. Livanos & Co. Inc., New York (two ships)	12,000d	Tankers
Bernh. Hanssen & Co. Flekkefjord	12,500d	Tanker
Matapan Shipping Co, Ltd.	9,900d	Cargo
Drake Shipping Co. Ltd.	9,900d	Cargo
Ellerman & Papayanni Lines (two ships)	5,100d	Cargo
China Navigation Co. Ltd. (two ships)	3,110d	Cargo
Cla Sud Americana de Vapores, Valparaiso	8,000g	Ore carrier

Greenock Dockyard Co. Ltd., Greenock

Clan Line Steamers Ltd. (three ships)	8,400g	Cargo and pass.
K. W. Hansen, Bergen	11,700g	Tanker
Hadley Shipping Co. Ltd.	11,700g	Tanker
Empire Transport Co. Ltd.	11,700g	Tanker
Pacific Steam Navigation Co. (two ships)	8,400g	Cargo and pass.
Clan Line Steamers Ltd. (two ships)	8,400g	Cargo and pass.

Hall, Russell & Co. Ltd., Aberdeen

London Power Co. Ltd. (two ships)	2,700d	Colliers
H. Kuhnle's Rederi A/S Bergen	8,000d	Cargo
North Thames Gas Board	2,700d	Collier
A/S Ganger Rolf (Fred Olsen & Co.) Oslo (three ships)	1,500d	Cargo
Government of Iceland (three ships)	–	Trawlers
Bruusgaard Kiosteruds Skibs, Oslo (two ships)	2,300d	Cargo

William Hamilton & Co. Ltd., Port Glasgow

Th. Brovig, Farsund	13,500d	Tanker
Harry Borthen & Co., A/S, Oslo	13,500d	Tanker
Th. Brovig (two ships)	16,000d	Tankers
Norwegian owners (two ships)	13,500d	Tankers
Hain Steamship Co. Ltd.	9,600d	Cargo
Australind Steam Shipping Co. Ltd.	9,500d	Cargo

Harland & Wolff Ltd., Belfast

Bombay Steam Navigation Co. Ltd.	3,800g	Pass. and cargo
Bombay Steam Navigation Co. Ltd.	1,200g	Pass. and cargo
Indian Co-operative Navigation & Trading Co. Ltd.	1,200g	Pass. and cargo
Alfred Holt & Company (two ships)	11,750g	Cargo and pass.
Moss Hutchison Line Ltd.	4,500d	Cargo
Anglo-Saxon Petroleum Co. Ltd.	28,000d	Tanker
British Tanker Co. Ltd. (three ships)	12,000d	Tankers
Sigurd Herlofson & Co. A/S, Oslo	24,000d	Tanker
Shaw Savill & Albion Co. Ltd. (two ships)	14,900g	Refrig. cargo
Viriks Rederi A/S, Sandefjord	12,000d	Tanker
Union-Castle Line	17,500g	Pass. and refrig. cargo
Tanker Corporation, Panama City	12,500d	Tanker
Cia. Argentina de Pesca S.A. Buenos Aires	23,000g	Whaling factory
Alfred Holt & Co.	11,750g	Cargo
Alfred Holt & Co.	9,000g	Cargo
Lorentzen's Rederi Co, Oslo	24,000d	Tanker
Moltzau & Christensen, Oslo	12,000d	Tanker
Olav Ringdal, Oslo	12,000d	Tanker
A/S Mosvold Shipping Co., Farsund	24,500d	Tanker

Hunting & Son Ltd.	12,000d	Tanker
Fred Olsen & Co., Oslo	24,000d	Tanker
Common Brothers Ltd.	12,000d	Tanker
British Tanker Co. Ltd.	28,000d	Tanker

Harland & Wolff Ltd., Govan

British Tanker Co. Ltd. (three ships)	12,250d	Tankers
A/S Borgestad, Porsgrund	12,200d	Tanker
Per Gjerding, Bergen	12,000d	Tanker
Eagle Oil & Shipping Co. Ltd.	15,000d	Tanker

R. & W. Hawthorn, Leslie & Co. Ltd., Hebburn

British Tanker Co. Ltd.	11,200g	Tanker
Shaw, Savill & Albion Co. Ltd.	9,600g	Refrig. cargo
Athel Line Ltd. (two ships)	11,200g	Molasses tankers
Athel Line Ltd.	7,400g	Molasses tanker
Alcoa Steamship Co. Inc., New York (two ships)	6,900g	Ore carriers
British Tanker Co. Ltd.	11,200g	Tanker
Athel Line Ltd.	9,050g	Molasses tanker
Port Line Ltd.	8,000g	Cargo and pass.
Overseas Tankship Corporation, New York (two ships)	16,500g	Tankers
British Tanker Co. Ltd.	28,000d	Tanker

Sir James Laing & Sons Ltd., Sunderland

British Tanker Co. Ltd.	16,000d	Tanker
Leif Hoegh & Co., Oslo (two ships)	23,000d	Tankers
Skibs. A/S Arnstein, Oslo (two ships)	15,000d	Tankers
Thorvald Berg, Tonsberg	15,000d	Tanker
British Tanker Co. Ltd. (two ships)	12,250d	Tankers
Counties Ship Management Co. Ltd. (three ships)	15,000d	Tankers
John I. Jacobs & Co. Ltd.	17,250d	Tanker
Sir R. Ropner & Co. Ltd. (two ships)	7,750d	Cargo and pass.
Lykiardopulo & Co. Ltd.	15,000d	Tanker

Lithgows Ltd., Port Glasgow

Scindia Steam Navigation Co. Ltd. (two ships)	9,400d	Cargo
Kr. Jebsen Jnr., Bergen	13,500d	Tanker
Skibs. A/S Dalfonn, Stavanger	13,500d	Tanker
British Tanker Co. Ltd. (three ships)	12,250d	Tankers
Bergenske Damps., Bergen	13,500d	Tanker
Nile Steamship Co. Ltd.	9,300d	Cargo
Hector Whaling Ltd.	13,500d	Tanker
Hector Whaling Ltd.	16,000d	Tanker
Asiatic Steam Navigation Co. Ltd.	5,500d	Cargo
Stamers Rederi A/S, Bergen	13,500d	Tanker
Skips A/S Sydhav, Oslo	16,000d	Tanker
T. & J. Harrison	5,000d	Cargo
United Steam Navigation Co. Ltd. (Mungo Campbell & Co. Ltd., managers)	13,500d	Tanker

British & Burmese Steam   — Cargo
Navigation Co. Ltd.
(two ships)
Alexander Shipping Co. Ltd.   15,500d Tanker

Wm. Pickersgill & Sons Ltd., Sunderland
British Electricity Authority   1,300g Colliers
(three ships)
Alfred Falter, New York   2,805g Cargo
Moss Hutchison Line Ltd.   3,575g Cargo
British Electricity Authority   3,370g Colliers
(four ships)

John Readhead & Sons Ltd., South Shields
Strick Line Ltd.   8,000g Cargo
Hain Steamship Co. Ltd.   5,760g Cargo
(two ships)
Strick Line Ltd.   8,000g Cargo and
                                        pass.
Strick Line Ltd.   7,200g Cargo

**Scotts' Shipbuilding & Engineering Co. Ltd.,
Greenock**
China Navigation Co. Ltd.   7,414g Passenger
China Navigation Co. Ltd.   4,000g Pass. and
                                        cargo
Bermuda & West Indies   3,724g Cargo
Steamship Co. Ltd.
China Navigation Co. Ltd.   8,000g Cargo and
(two ships)   pass.
Star Whaling Co. Ltd., Jersey 16,500d Tanker
Northam Steamship Co. Ltd.   16,500d Tanker
Tonsberg Hvalfangeri A/S,   14,000d Whaling
Tonsberg   tanker
Elder Dempster Lines Ltd.   9,600d Cargo
(two ships)

Short Brothers Ltd., Sunderland
Cia. Lama de Vapores A/S,   3,400d Cargo
Panama City
"Pacific" A/S,   3,400d Cargo
Copenhagen
Foreign owners   10,000d Cargo
Rederi A/B Soya,   10,000d Tanker
Stockholm
Stanhope Steamship Co. Ltd.   10,000d Cargo
Foreign owners   10,000d Cargo

Smith's Dock Co. Ltd., South Bank
Norwegian owners   — Whale
(seven ships)   catchers
Chr. Salvesen & Co.   — Whale
(eight ships)   catchers
Anglo-Saxon Petroleum   6,100d Tankers
Co. Ltd. (two ships)
Anglo-Saxon Petroleum   9,250d Tanker
Co. Ltd.
Athel Line Ltd.   10,000d Tanker
Athel Line Ltd.   12,500d Tanker
British Tanker Co. Ltd.   8,380d Tanker
Anglo-Saxon Petroleum   7,940d Tanker
Co. Ltd.
S. G. Livanos, Piraeus   14,400d Tanker
H. E. Moss & Co. (two ships)   14,500d Tankers
Hunting & Son Ltd.   14,500d Tanker
Cia. Argentina de Pesca S.A.,   — Whale
Buenos Aires (five ships)   catchers

Devon Fishing Co. Ltd.   — Trawlers
(three ships)
Northern Fishing Co.,   — Trawlers
(Hull) Ltd. (three ships)

Alexander Stephen & Sons Ltd., Linthouse
French Government   5,100g Cargo
Federal Steam Navigation   9,940g Cargo
Co. Ltd.
Argentine Government   7,500g Cargo and
                                        pass.
Union Steam Ship Co. of   5,170d Cargo
New Zealand Ltd.
Ellerman Lines Ltd.   7,000g Cargo
(two ships)
New Zealand Shipping Co. Ltd.   9,000g Cargo
Elder Dempster Lines Ltd.   14,000g Passenger

**Swan, Hunter & Wigham Richardson Ltd.,
Wallsend-on-Tyne**
British Tanker Co. Ltd.   10,985g Tanker
Ellerman Lines Ltd.   7,580g Cargo
Alfred Holt & Company   11,500g Cargo and
                                        pass.
Hvalfanger A/S Vestfold,   8,760g Tanker
Sandefjord
Argentine Government   8,060g Tanker
Hilmar Reksten, Bergen   17,270g Tanker
British Tanker Co. Ltd.   10,985g Tankers
(two ships)
Anglo-Saxon Petroleum   18,620g Tankers
Co. Ltd. (two ships)
Rafen & Loennechen, Tonsberg   15,000d Tanker
A/S Havtank, Oslo   8,760g Tanker
Cunard White Star Ltd.   8,830g Cargo
British Tanker Co. Ltd.   18,200g Tanker

Neptune Works, Newcastle-upon-Tyne
Cia. Nacional de   12,950g Pass. and
Navegacao, Lisbon   cargo
British Tanker Co. Ltd.   8,600g Tanker
British India S.N. Co. Ltd.   7,600g Cargo
British India S.N. Co. Ltd.   7,150g Cargo
Soc. Generale de Transports   16,100g Pass. and
Maritimes a Vapeur, Paris   cargo
British Tanker Co. Ltd.   8,700g Tankers
(two ships)
British India Steam   7,150g Cargo
Navigation Co. Ltd.
(two ships)
Rederi A/B Svenska Lloyd,   7,700g Pass. and
Gothenburg   cargo

Joseph L. Thompson & Sons Ltd., Sunderland
Ellerman Lines Ltd.   7,200g Cargo
Silver Line Ltd.   6,200g Cargo
Indo-China Steam Navigation   6,200g Cargo
Co. Ltd.
A/S Thor Dahl, Sandefjord   10,150g Tanker
Anglo-Saxon Petroleum   5,041g Tankers
Co. Ltd. (two ships)
Silver Line Ltd. (two ships)   6,200g Cargo
British Tanker Co. Ltd.   6,100g Tankers
(three ships)
Athel Line Ltd. (two ships)   12,250g Tankers
Rolf Wigand, Bergen   15,000d Tanker
Leif Hoegh & Co., Oslo   15,000d Tankers
(two ships)

John I. Thornycroft & Co. Ltd., Southampton

Crown Agents for Colonies	17g	Launch
Shell Petroleum Co. Ltd.	175g	Tug
Fred Olsen & Co., Oslo (hull only)	5,000g	Pass. and cargo
Crown Agents for Colonies	89g	Vehicle ferry

Vickers-Armstrongs Ltd., Barrow-in-Furness

P.&O. Steam Navigation Company	28,250g	Pass. and cargo
P.&O. Steam Navigation Company	24,000g	Pass. and cargo
Argentine State Merchant Fleet (two ships)	18,000g	Pass. and cargo
Orient Steam Navigation Co. Ltd.	28,250g	Pass. and cargo
British Tanker Co. Ltd.	28,000d	Tanker

Vickers-Armstrongs Ltd., Walker-on-Tyne

Alfred Holt & Company	8,200g	Cargo and pass.
New Zealand Shipping Co. Ltd.	19,000g	Pass. and cargo
Alfred Holt & Company (two ships)	10,000g	Cargo and pass.
Alfred Holt & Company	8,200g	Cargo and pass.
Ellerman Lines Ltd. (two ships)	7,500g	Cargo and pass.
Prince Line Ltd. (two ships)	7,500g	Pass. and cargo
A/S Jensen's Rederei II, Arendal	24,500d	Tanker
Aksjerederiet Julian, Bergen	24,500d	Tanker
Furness Withy & Co. Ltd.	14,500g	Passenger
Ellerman & Bucknall S.S. Co. Ltd.	12,500g	Pass. and cargo

APPENDIX IV

Extracts from the April 1953 edition of "New Construction in Hand or on Order" — Merchant Shipbuilding in British yards.

Barclay, Curle & Co. Ltd., Whiteinch, Glasgow

Melsom & Melsom, Larvik	18,000d	Tanker
Rafen & Loennechan, Tonsberg	15,000d	Tanker
British India S.N. Co. Ltd. (two ships)	10,000g	Cargo
Eastern & Australian S.S. Co. Ltd.	10,000g	Cargo
Ellerman Lines Ltd. (two ships)	8,000g	Cargo
British India S.N. Co. Ltd.	20,000g	Transport
Watts, Watts & Co. Ltd.	7,600g	Cargo

Bartram & Sons Ltd., South Dock, Sunderland

Lamport & Holt Line Ltd.	9,800d	Cargo and pass.
Rederi A/B, Soya, Stockholm	10,000d	Cargo
Buries Markes Ltd.	9,600d	Cargo
Monarch Steamship Co. Ltd.	10,000d	Cargo
Haldin & Co. Ltd. (two ships)	10,900d	Cargo
Houlder Bros. & Co. Ltd.	10,950d	Cargo
North Shipping Co. Ltd.	9,900d	Cargo
Los Sons & A. K. Pezas, Chios (two ships)	10,850d	Cargo
J. A. Cosmas, San Francisco (two ships)	{ 10,700d Cargo { 10,950d Cargo •	
Alva Steamship Co. Ltd., London	10,850d	Cargo
N. S. Pateras & Sons, London	10,850d	Cargo
Greek owners	16,500d	Tanker
Marine Enterprises, Ltd. (Lyras Bros., Ltd., London)	16,000d	Tanker
B.I.S.C. (Ore), Ltd.	12-14,000d	Ore carrier
Cia. Achilles de Navegacion S.A., Panama	7,000g	Cargo
Cia. Farallon de Navegacion S.A., Panama	7,000g	Cargo

Blyth Dry Docks and Shipbuilding Co. Ltd., Blyth

British Oil Shipping Co. Ltd.	18,000d	Tanker
British owners (two ships)	1,500d	Tankers
Straits Steamship Co. Ltd.	725d	Cargo and pass.
Australian Government (two ships)	10,000d	Ore carriers
Dalhousie Steam & Motorship Co. Ltd.	10,500d	Cargo
Greek owners	10,500d	Cargo
Olsen & Ugelstad, Oslo	18,000d	Tanker
J. Ludwig Mowinckels Rederi, Bergen	18,000d	Tanker

Blythswood Shipbuilding Co. Ltd., Scotstoun

Cia de Vapores S.A., Panama (Lyras Bros., Ltd., London)	12,750g	Tanker
Lowland Tanker Co. Ltd. (two ships)	11,200g	Tankers
Trinidad Leaseholds Ltd.	9,700g	Tanker
British Tanker Co. Ltd.	11,200g	Tanker
Skibs. A/S William Hansens Rederi, Bergen	2,550g	Tanker
Baltic Trading Co. Ltd.	13,700g	Tanker
Bruusgaard, Kjosterud & Co., Drammen	11,000g	Tanker
Cia. Petrolera de Transportes S.A., Panama	18,750g	Tanker
Alvion Steamship Corp., Panama	13,700g	Tanker

John Brown & Co. Ltd., Clydebank

New Zealand Shipping Co. Ltd.	12,000d	Refrig. cargo
New Zealand Shipping Co. Ltd. (two ships)	4,250g	Cargo
P.&O. S.N. Co.	28,000g	Passenger
British Tanker Co. Ltd. (three ships)	32,000d	Tankers
Esso Petroleum Co. Ltd.	26,500d	Tanker
Tidewater Commercial Co. Inc.	19,000d	Tanker
Alvion Steamship Corp. Panama (three ships)	32,000d	Tankers
New Zealand Shipping Co. Ltd. (two ships)	—	Cargo
Admiralty	4,000 (displacement)	Royal yacht
Cunard Steam-Ship Co. Ltd. (two ships)	20,000g	Passenger
New Zealand Shipping Co. Ltd.	—	Cargo
P.&O. S.N. Co. (two ships)	—	Cargo

Burntisland Shipbuilding Co. Ltd., Burntisland

Constantine Shipping Co. Ltd.	1,270g	Cargo
Alexander Shipping Co. Ltd. (Houlder Bros & Co. Ltd., managers)	5,550g	Cargo
Johnston Warren Lines Ltd. (Furness, Withy & Co. Ltd., managers) (two ships)	3,550g	Cargo liners
Prince Line Ltd. (Furness, Withy & Co. Ltd., managers)	3,550g	Cargo liner
The Power Steamship Co. Ltd. (O. Gross & Sons, Ltd., managers) (two ships)	6,300g	Cargo
Cia. de Navegacion Oriental de Panama (Phocean Ship Agency Ltd.)	8,500g	Cargo
Pan-Ore Steamship Co. Inc. (Associates of Alcoa Steamship Co. Inc.), New York (two ships)	6,650g	Bauxite ore carriers
Saguenay Terminals Ltd. (Associates of the Aluminium Company of Canada), Montreal	6,600g	Bauxite ore and oil carrier
Fomentador Cia Naviera S.A., Panama (two ships)	5,700g	Cargo
Tramp Chartering Corporation, Panama	5,700g	Cargo
The Dundee, Perth and London Shipping Co. Ltd.	1,875g	Cargo
Alvion Steamship Corp., Panama	5,700g	Cargo
Dover Hill Steamship Co. Ltd.	5,700g	Cargo
Sarac Compania Naviera S.A., Panama	5,700g	Cargo
Currie Line Ltd.	7,500g	Bulk carrier
Huddart Parker Ltd., Melbourne	2,500g	Cargo
Prince Line Ltd. (Furness, Withy & Co. Ltd., managers) (two ships)	2,360g	Cargo liners
Wm. Cory & Son Ltd. (two ships)	3,400g	Colliers

111

Caledon Shipbuilding & Engineering Co. Ltd., Dundee

H. Hogarth & Sons Ltd.	12,000g	Tanker
Temple Steamship Co. Ltd.	4,950g	Cargo
Alfred Holt & Company	7,700g	Cargo
Watts, Watts & Co. Ltd.	7,800g	Cargo
Sir R. Ropner & Co. (Management) Ltd.	6,800g	Cargo
H. Hogarth & Sons Ltd.	5,500g	Cargo
Iver Bugge, Larvik	13,500g	Tanker
Alfred Holt & Company	8,500g	Cargo
Straits Steamship Co. Ltd.	1,350g	Pass. and cargo
Ellerman Lines Ltd.	8,000g	Cargo
Alfred Holt & Company	8,300g	Cargo
Ellerman Lines Ltd.	3,910g	Refrig. cargo
Watts, Watts & Co. Ltd. (two ships)	7,800g	Cargo
Sarawak Steamship Co. Ltd.	2,300g	Cargo and pass.
Athel Line Ltd.	9,160g	Tanker

Cammell Laird & Co. Ltd., Birkenhead

Anglo-Saxon Petroleum Co. Ltd. (five ships)	18,000d	Tankers
Eagle Oil & Shipping Co. Ltd.	18,000d	Tanker
John Holt Line Ltd.	6,000g	Cargo
British Tanker Co. Ltd.	16,000d	Tanker
Esso Petroleum Co. Ltd. (three ships)	26,500d	Tankers
Anglo-Saxon Petroleum Co. Ltd. (two ships)	31,000d	Tankers
Burmah Oil Co. (Tankers) Ltd.	8,400d	Tanker
Pan-Ore Steamship Co. Inc., New York	31,000d	Bauxite ore-carrier
Eagle Oil & Shipping Co. Ltd. (two ships)	18,000d	Tankers
S. G. Embiricos Ltd. (for clients)	10,000d	Cargo
Manchester Liners Ltd.	8,900d	Cargo and pass.
Ellerman Lines Ltd.	10,500d	Cargo
Liverpool Screw Towing & Lighterage Co. Ltd. (two ships)	—	Tugs
Sugar Line Ltd., London	9,500d	Bulk sugar carrier
Booth Steamship Co. Ltd	7,700g	Pass. and cargo
Coast Lines Ltd.	1,400d	Cargo
H. E. Moss and Co.	18,000d	Tanker
British & Continental Steamship Co. Ltd. (two ships)	1,540d	Cargo
Irish Shipping Ltd. (two ships)	9,000d	Cargo
Eagle Oil and Shipping Co. Ltd.	31,000d	Tanker
British Tanker Co. Ltd.	32,000d	Tanker
Anglo-Saxon Petroleum Co. Ltd.	18,000d	Tanker
Isle of Man Steam Packet Co. Ltd.	2,500g	Passenger

Charles Connell & Co. Ltd., Scotstoun

Wilhelm Wilhelmsen, Oslo (two ships)	18,000d	Tankers
Ben Line Steamers Ltd. (four ships)	12,000d	Cargo
Norscot Shipping Co. Ltd.	18,500d	Tanker
Fearnley & Eger, Oslo (two ships)	18,000d	Tankers

James Nourse Ltd.	10,000d	Cargo
Wilhelm Wilhelmsen, Oslo (two ships)	10,000d	Cargo
Alscot Shipping Co. Ltd., Glasgow	18,000d	Tanker
Fearnley and Eger, Oslo (two ships)	10,000d	Cargo
Denholm Line Steamers Ltd., Glasgow (two ships)	9,670d	Cargo
Wilhelm Wilhelmsen, Oslo	8,000d	Cargo

John Crown & Sons Ltd., Sunderland

Olsen & Ugelstad, Oslo (two ships)	2,800d	Cargo
Rolf Wigand, Bergen	18,250d	Tanker
Silver Line Ltd.	10,000d	Cargo

William Denny & Bros. Ltd., Dumbarton

A. G. Pappadakis, Piraeus (two ships)	7,000g	Cargo
British & Burmese S.N. Co. Ltd.	5,600g	Cargo
Scottish Home Department	270g	Fishery protection
G. Nicolaou, Piraeus	7,000g	Cargo
Pacific Steam Navigation Co.	8,500g	Cargo
Railway Executive, Scottish Region	650g	Pass. and car ferry
Bowaters' Newfoundland Pulp & Paper Mills Ltd. (two ships)	7,500g	Newsprint Carriers
Indo-China Steam Navigation Co. Ltd.	7,000g	Cargo
O. Ditlev-Simonsen Jr., Oslo	7,000g	Cargo
David MacBrayne Ltd., Glasgow	1,000g	Pass. and cargo
Sundry small craft for shipment abroad.		

William Doxford & Sons Ltd., Pallion, Sunderland

Hunting & Son Ltd. (two ships)	11,400g	Tankers
Morel Ltd. (two ships)	5,500g	Cargo
British Tanker Co. Ltd.	11,300g	Tanker
Lowland Tanker Co. Ltd.	11,300g	Tanker
Rethymnis & Kulukundis Ltd., Syra (three ships)	6,600g	Cargo
Anchor Line Ltd.	5,700g	Cargo
Sir Wm. Reardon Smith and Sons Ltd. (four ships)	6,300g	Cargo
Cia. Panamena Europea Navegacion Ltda. (two ships)	11,400g	Tankers
J. & C. Harrison Ltd., (two ships)	6,700g	Cargo
Charente Steam Ship Co. Ltd. (Thos. and Jas. Harrison Ltd., managers) (two ships)	6,100g	Cargo
Andrew Weir Shipping & Trading Co. Ltd.	6,300g	Cargo

Fairfield Shipbuilding & Engineering Co. Ltd., Govan

Canadian Pacific Steamships Ltd.	22,500g	Pass. and cargo
Atlantic Oil Carriers Ltd. Monrovia	19,500d	Tanker
Global Transport Ltd., Panama (four ships)	12,500d	Cargo
Sociedad Tropica de Carga S.A.	18,000d	Tanker
Lowland Tanker Co. Ltd.	16,000d	Tanker
Liberian Navigation Corp. (four ships)	22,000d	Bulk ore carriers
Thor Thoresen & Co., Oslo	16,000d	Tanker
Bibby Line Ltd.	20,000g	Troopship.

Furness Shipbuilding Co. Ltd., Haverton Hill-on-Tees

Drake Shipping Co. Ltd.	18,200d	Tanker
London & Overseas	18,200d	Tankers
Freighters Ltd. (two ships)		
Cia. Armadora Transoceanica	24,500d	Tanker
S.A., Panama		
Erling H. Samuelsens	18,200d	Tanker
Rederi A/S, Oslo		
London and Overseas	24,750d	Tankers
Freighters Ltd. (two ships)		
Overseas Tankship (U.K.) Ltd.	16,500d	Tanker
Northern Steamships Ltd.,	24,500d	Tanker
Johannesburg		
Afran Transport Company	32,000d	Tankers
(two ships), Monrovia		
Soc. Transoceanica	16,300d	Tanker
Canopus S.A., Panama		
Drake Shipping Co. Ltd.	10,000d	Cargo
Nueva Vista Cia., Naviera	16,300d	Tanker
S.A., Panama		
Northern Steamships Ltd.,	10,000d	Cargo
Johannesburg		
Soc. Transoceanica	24,750d	Tanker
Canopus S.A., Panama		
Chr. Salvesen & Co.	18,200d	Tanker
Porto Alegre Cia. Naviera S.A.	24,750d	Tanker
Skips. A/S Corona,	18,200d	Tanker
Haugesund		
Iron Ore Transport Co. Ltd.	31,000d	Bulk/ore carrier
S. Ugelstads Rederi A/S,	32,000d	Tanker
Oslo		
Victoria Shipping Co. Ltd.	24,750d	Tanker
London & Overseas	24,750d	Tankers
Freighters Ltd. (three ships)		
Victoria Shipping Co. Ltd.	32,000d	Tanker
London & Overseas	24,750d	Tanker
Freighters Ltd.		
Halifax Overseas	24,750d	Tanker
Freighters Ltd.		
Acadia Overseas Freighters	24,750d	Tanker
(Halifax) Ltd.		
Vancouver Oriental Line,	24,750d	Tanker
Vancouver		
Falaise Steamship Co. Ltd.	24,750d	Tanker
Somerset Shipping Co. Ltd.	16,300d	Tanker
British Oil Shipping Co. Ltd.	16,300d	Tankers
(two ships)		
Progressive Investments Ltd.	32,000d	Tankers
(two ships)		
Ottawa Steamship Co. Ltd.	24,750d	Tanker
(Colouthros Ltd., London)		
Victoria Shipping Co. Ltd.	16,300d	Tankers
(two ships)		

William Gray & Co. Ltd., West Hartlepool

N. G. Livanos, Piraeus	10,000d	Cargo
Maritime Shipping &	10,000d	Cargo
Trading Co. Ltd.		
Irish Shipping Ltd.	8,850d	Cargo
Irish Shipping Ltd. (two ships)	9,500d	Cargo
Ore Carriers Ltd. (four ships)	9,000d	Ore carriers
Ore Carriers Ltd. (two ships)	9,000d	Ore carriers
Rederi Hans von Rettig &	8,735d	Cargo
A/B Wilh Bensow O/Y,		
Finland		
S. G. Livanos, Piraeus	12,500d	Cargo
H. P. Lenaghan & Sons Ltd.,	9,000d	Cargo
Belfast		
Elder Dempster Lines Ltd.	10,000d	Cargo
Ellerman Lines Ltd.	3,500d	Cargo
Cia. Armadora Transoceanica	10,000d	Cargo
S.A., Panama		

N. G. Livanos, Piraeus	10,000d	Cargo
A/S Mabella (K. Bruusgaard),	3,500d	Cargo
Drammen		
D/S Marna A/S, Norway	3,450d	Cargo
Irish Shipping Ltd.	3,150d	Tanker
Ellerman Lines Ltd. (two ships)	5,330d	Cargo
N. G. Livanos (two ships)	10,000d	Cargo
Soc. Paulista de Navegacao	10,000d	Cargo
Matarazzo Ltda., Santos	8,750d	
(two ships)		
Irish Shipping Ltd. (two ships)	9,500d	Cargo

Greenock Dockyard Co. Ltd., Greenock

Alva Steamship Co. Ltd.	16,500d	Tanker
Clan Line Steamers Ltd.	11,000d	Cargo and pass.
Clan Line Steamers Ltd.	10,000d	Cargo and pass.
Scottish Tanker Co. Ltd.	16,300d	Tankers
(two ships)		
Pacific Steam Navigation	11,000d	Cargo and pass.
Company (two ships)		
Clan Line Steamers Ltd.	10,000d	Cargo and pass.
(three ships)		
Clan Line Steamers Ltd.	10,000d	Cargo and pass.
(three ships)		

Hall, Russell & Co. Ltd., Aberdeen

Crown Agents for Colonies	4,000d	Collier
(for Nigeria)		
Wm. Cory & Son Ltd.	4,600d	Collier
A/S Rederiet Odfjell, Bergen	7,800d	Cargo
North Thames Gas Board	4,600d	Colliers
(Stephenson Clarke Ltd.)		
(three ships)		
Associated Humber Lines	1,100d	Cargo
(two ships)		
British Electricity Authority	4,600d	Colliers
(three ships)		
A/S Rederiet Odfjell, Bergen	6,400d	Cargo
J. & A. Brown & Abermain,	1,800d	Collier
Seaham Collieries Ltd., Sydney		
A/S Ganger Rolf	2,500d	Cargo
Eilert Lund, Bergen	3,000d	Cargo
Esso Petroleum Co. Ltd.	2,300d	Bitumen carrier
Silvertown Services Ltd.,	5,000d	Bulk sugar carriers
London (two ships)		
D.S.I.R. (on behalf of Torry	—	Research trawler
Research Station, Aberdeen)		
Canadian National Railways	—	Cargo and pass.
(two ships)		
McIlwralth, McEacharn Ltd.,	5,500d	Cargo
Melbourne		
Australind Steamships Pty. Ltd.	5,500d	Cargo

William Hamilton & Co. Ltd., Port Glasgow

Alva Steamship Co. Ltd.	11,700g	Tanker
Blue Star Line Ltd.	11,700g	Tanker
Hain Steamship Co. Ltd.	9,200d	Cargo
Thos. & Jno. Brocklebank Ltd.	8,000g	Cargo
(two ships)		
Johan Gerrard, Kristiansand	17,500d	Tanker
Harry Borthen & Co. A/S, Oslo	13,500d	Tanker
British Tanker Co. Ltd.	16,000d	Tanker
Hellenic Lines Ltd., Piraeus	10,500d	Cargo
(two ships)		
Th. Brovig, Farsund	16,000d	Tanker
Cunard Steam-Ship Co. Ltd.	3,300g	Cargo
(three ships)		
S. G. Andreadis, Athens	16,500d	Tankers
(two ships)		

113

Halfdan Kuhnle, Bergen 17,500d Tanker
Hain Steamship Co. Ltd. 9,500d Cargo
Halfdan Kuhnle, Bergen 9,500d Cargo

Harland & Wolff Ltd., Belfast
Elder Dempster Lines Ltd. 7,500d Cargo and
pass.
Shaw Savill & Albion Co. Ltd. 10,700g Refrig.
cargo
Andrew Weir Shipping & 9,000d Cargo
Trading Co. Ltd. (five ships)
P.&O. S.N. Co. 28,000g Passenger
British Tanker Co. Ltd. 32,000d Tankers
(two ships)
British Tanker Co. Ltd. 14,000d Tanker
Anders Jahre & Co., A/S,
Sandefjord 18,500d Tankers
(two ships)
Anglo-Saxon Petroleum Co. Ltd. 18,000d Tankers
(four ships)
Anglo-Saxon Petroleum 31,000d Tankers
Co. Ltd. (two ships)
Alfred Holt & Company 7,700g Cargo and
(two ships) pass.
Ulster Steamship Co. Ltd. 5,700g Cargo and
pass.
Hans Kiaer & Co. A/S, 12,000d Tanker
Fredrikstad (A/S Fjeld)
Royal Mail Lines Ltd. 9,600d Cargo and
pass.
Port Line Ltd. 11,500d Refrig.
cargo
Skibs A/S Dalfonn 29,200d Tanker
(Mr. Sigval Bergesen),
Stavanger
Svend Foyn Bruun, Tonsberg 13,200d Tanker
Moltzau and Christensen, 13,500d Tanker
Oslo
Anders Jahre, Sandefjord 13,200d Tankers
(two ships)
Borgestad A/S, Borgestad 6,000g Cargo
Union-Castle Line (two ships) 7,450g Cargo
Pacific Steam Navigation 19,320g Passenger
Company
Shaw Savill & Albion Co. Ltd. 20,000g Passenger
Olav Ringdal, Oslo 13,500d Tanker

Harland & Wolff Ltd., Govan
British Tanker Co. Ltd., 14,000d Tankers
(two ships)
Blandford Shipping Co. Ltd. 18,000d Tanker
Port Line Ltd. 6,400g Refrig
cargo
Skibs. A/S Belships Co. Ltd., 18,500d Tanker
Oslo
A. O. Andersen Shipping Co., 19,000d Tanker
A/S, Oslo
Prince Line Ltd. (two ships) 10,000d Cargo
British Phosphate 12,000d Pass. and
Commissioners, Melbourne cargo
Johnston Warren Lines Ltd. 10,000d Cargo
Arth. H. Mathiesen, Oslo 18,700d Tanker

R. & W. Hawthorn, Leslie & Co. Ltd., Hebburn
Overseas Tankship (U.K.) Ltd. 16,500d Tankers
(two ships)
Moor Line Ltd. 9,350d Cargo
British Tanker Co. Ltd. 16,000d Tanker
Lowland Tanker Co. Ltd. 16,000d Tanker

Anglo-Saxon Petroleum Co. Ltd. 18,000d Tankers
(four ships)
Athel Line Ltd. 10,300d Tanker
Moor Line Ltd. (two ships) 9,350d Cargo
Anglo-Saxon Petroleum Co. Ltd. 31,000d Tanker
Athel Line Ltd. 10,300d Tanker
Sugar Line Ltd., London 9,500d Bulk sugar
(two ships) Carriers
Anglo-Saxon Petroleum 18,000d Tanker
Co. Ltd.
Anglo-Saxon Petroleum 31,000d Tanker
Co. Ltd.
Overseas Tankship (U.K.) Ltd. 18,000d Tanker
British Tanker Co. Ltd. 32,000d Tanker
Hunting & Son Ltd. 31,000d Tanker
Houlder Bros. & Co. Ltd. 18,000d Tanker

Sir James Laing & Sons Ltd., Sunderland
Alva Steamship Co. Ltd. 18,000d Tanker
Hunting Steamship Co. Ltd. 16,500d Tanker
John I. Jacobs & Co. Ltd. 18,000d Tanker
Sir R. Ropner & Co. 9,100d Cargo
(Management) Ltd. liner
British Tanker Co. Ltd. 16,000d Tanker
Thorvald Berg, Tonsberg 18,000d Tanker
Sir R. Ropner & Co. 18,000d Tanker
(Management) Ltd.
Lowland Tanker Co. Ltd. 16,000d Tanker
S. H. Smith Sorensen, Arendal 26,400d Tanker
A/S Tank (Hjalmar Bjorge, 18,000d Tanker
Managers), Oslo

Lithgows Ltd., Port Glasgow
British Tanker Co. Ltd. 16,000d Tankers
(two ships)
McCowen & Gross Ltd. 16,500d Tanker
Anglo-Saxon Petroleum Co. Ltd. 18,000d Tankers
(four ships)
Temple Steamship Co. Ltd. 9,400d Cargo
British & Burmese S.N. 10,000d Cargo
Co. Ltd. (three ships)
Skibs. A/S Ringfonn, 18,000d Tanker
Stavanger
A. F. Klaveness & Co., 18,000d Tanker
A/S., Oslo
Ayrshire Navigation Co., Ltd. 14,000d Ore-carrier
United Whalers Ltd. 18,000d Tanker
Anchor Line Ltd. 9,450d Cargo
(three ships)
Scottish Ore Carriers Ltd., 9,000d Ore-carrier
Glasgow
Blandford Shipping Co. Ltd. 18,000d Tanker
Wes'fal Larsen & Co., A/S, 16,500d Tankers
Bergen (two ships)
A. F. Klaveness & Co., A/S, 9,600d Cargo
Oslo (four ships)
N. R. Bugge Skibs A/S and
A/S, Hektor, Tonsberg 20,000d Tanker
Lyle Shipping Co., Ltd. 10,000d Cargo
Glasgow (two ships)
B. I. S. C. (Ore), Ltd. 12-14,000d Ore
(six ships) carriers
Mogul Line Ltd., Bombay 7,500d Pilgrim
and cargo

Wm. Pickersgill & Sons Ltd., Sunderland

Morel Ltd.	9,000d Cargo
Trader Navigation Co. Ltd.	9,500d Cargo
Bolton Steam Shipping Co. Ltd.	10,000d Cargo
Larrinaga Steamship Co. Ltd. (two ships)	10,000d Cargo
H. Hogarth & Sons Ltd.	9,000d Cargo
North Thames Gas Board	4,600d Collier
Wm. France Fenwick & Co. Ltd. (two ships)	10,000d Cargo
British Electricity Authority	4,600d Collier
Union Industrielle et Maritime, Paris	5,600d Collier
C. Ostberg, Oslo	10,000d Cargo
Lamport & Holt Line Ltd.	7,000d Cargo
Larrinaga Steamship Co. Ltd.	10,000d Cargo
Alvion Steamship Corp., Panama	10,000d Cargo
P. Lodding, Oslo	10,000d Cargo
Lamport & Holt Line Ltd.	9,500d Cargo

John Readhead & Sons Ltd., South Shields

Wm. France Fenwick & Co. Ltd.	6,190g Cargo
Strick Line Ltd. (three ships)	7,400g Cargo liners
Kaye, Son & Co. Ltd.	9,600g Cargo
H. Hogarth & Sons Ltd., (three ships)	9,400g Cargo
Maritime Shipping & Trading Co. Ltd.	8,000g Cargo
Barberry's Steamship Co. Ltd.	8,900d Newsprint carrier
Bristol City Line of Steamships Ltd.	8,500d Cargo
Foreign owners (two ships)	10,000d Cargo
Nicolas G. Nicolaou, Athens	10,000d Cargo
Stag Line Ltd.	8,000d Cargo

Henry Robb Ltd., Leith

Manchester Ship Canal Company	160g Tug
Rodney Steamship Co. Ltd.	5,500d Cargo
A. F. Henry & MacGregor Ltd.	900d Cargo
Associated Portland Cement Manufacturers Ltd.	1,200d Coaster
Sarawak Steamship Co., Ltd.	1,600g Cargo and pass.
Ellerman's Wilson Line Ltd. (two ships)	2,490d Cargo
Ellerman's Wilson Line Ltd.	1,800d Cargo
Currie Line Ltd.	1,850d Cargo
Union Steam Ship Co. of New Zealand Ltd.	2,100d Cargo
Union Steam Ship Co. of New Zealand Ltd. (two ships)	3,000d Cargo
Crown Agents for Colonies	— Grab hopper dredger

Scotts' Shipbuilding & Engineering Co. Ltd., Greenock

Andreadis (London) Ltd.	17,000d Tanker
Markos P. Nomikos, Piraeus	17,000d Tanker
Lowland Tanker Co. Ltd.	16,000d Tanker
Elder Dempster Lines Ltd.	10,000d Cargo

British India S.N. Co. Ltd.	10,000d Cargo
Sugar Line Ltd., London	9,500d Bulk sugar carrier
Star Whaling Co. Ltd., London	17,260d Tanker
Overseas Tankship (U.K.) Ltd.	18,000d Tanker
Athel Line Ltd.	13,000d Tanker
British India S.N. Co. Ltd.	10,000d Cargo
Soc. Carga Oceanica, S/A Panama (A. Lusi, Ltd.)	17,000d Tanker

Short Brothers Ltd., Sunderland

Alva Steamship Co. Ltd., London	10,000d Cargo
Parana Cia. de Vapores S.A., Panama	10,250d Cargo
A. G. Pappadakis, London	10,000d Cargo
D/S A/S Sverre, Bergen (two ships)	9,250d Cargo
A. K. Pezas & Transolas Cia. Naviera S.A., Chios	10,000d Cargo
Norwegian America Line	10,250d Cargo
Bj. Ruud-Petersen, Oslo	10,250d Cargo
Cia Farallon de Navegacion, Panama	11,000d Cargo
Court Line Ltd.	10,000d Cargo
Klosters Rederi A/S, Oslo	9,400d Cargo
Thomasson Shipping Co. Ltd.	10,000d Cargo

Smith's Dock Co. Ltd., South Bank

Silver Line Ltd.	16,500d Tanker
Bolton Steam Shipping Co. Ltd.	16,000d Tanker
British Tanker Co. Ltd.	16,000d Tanker
H. E. Moss & Co. Ltd.	16,500d Tanker
Anglo-Saxon Petroleum Co. Ltd. (five ships)	18,000d Tankers
Klosters Rederi A/S, Oslo	18,000d Tanker
A/S J. Ludwig Mowinckels Rederi, Bergen	16,700d Tanker
Eagle Tanker Co. Ltd. (two ships)	18,000d Tankers
A/S Bruusgaard, Drammen	3,600d Cargo
Bergens Kulkompani A/S	4,000d Tanker
Bolton Steam Shipping Co. Ltd. (two ships)	10,000d Cargo
Sugar Line Ltd., London (two ships)	9,500d Bulk sugar carriers
Anders Jahre & Co. A/S, Sandefjord	4,000d Tanker
Burnett Steamship Co. Ltd.	5,500d Cargo

Alexander Stephen & Sons Ltd., Linthouse

Greek Line (Goulandris Bros.)	20,000g Pass. and cargo
New Zealand Shipping Co. Ltd.	— Cargo
Bergenske Dampskibs, Bergen (three ships)	6,800d Cargo
P.&O. S.N. Co. Ltd. (two ships)	11,500d Cargo and pass.
P.&O. S.N. Co. Ltd.	10,500d Cargo and pass.
Ellerman Lines Ltd. (two ships)	10,500d Cargo
Union Steam Ship Co. of New Zealand Ltd. (two ships)	5,300d Cargo

Swan, Hunter & Wigham Richardson Ltd., Wallsend-on-Tyne

Hilmar Reksten, Bergen	31,000d	Tanker
Hopemount Shipping Co. Ltd.	18,600d	Tanker
Anglo-Saxon Petroleum Co. Ltd. (two ships)	18,000d	Tankers
Anglo-Saxon Petroleum Co. Ltd. (two ships)	18,000d	Tankers
Burmah Oil Co. (Tankers) Ltd.	8,400d	Tanker
British Tanker Co. Ltd.	32,000d	Tanker
Port Line Ltd.	11,000d	Refrig. cargo
Helmer Staubo & Co., Oslo	8,500d	Cargo
Anglo-Saxon Petroleum Co. Ltd.	28,000d	Tanker
Rio Cape Line Ltd.	12,000d	Cargo
M. A. Hanna Co., Cleveland, Ohio	32,000d	Bulk ore carrier
Den norske Amerikalinje, Oslo	—	Passenger
Helmer Staubo & Co., Oslo	15,000d	Tanker
Rafen & Loennechen, Tonsberg	18,600d	Tanker
Anglo-Saxon Petroleum Co. Ltd.	31,000d	Tanker

Neptune Works, Newcastle-upon-Tyne

A/R Caloric, Bergen	18,000d	Tanker
British Tanker Co. Ltd.	16,000d	Tanker
Cia. Nav. Hesperia S.A., Panama	5,750g	Cargo
Lowland Tanker Co. Ltd.	16,000d	Tanker
Cable & Wireless Ltd.	2,500d	Cable ship
Tramp Chartering Corp. of Panama (A. Lusi Ltd.)	5,830g	Cargo
Tramp Chartering Corp. of Panama (A. Lusi Ltd.) (two ships)	6,800g	Cargo
The Queen Line Ltd. and the Cadogan Steamship Co. Ltd. (Thos. Dunlop & Sons, managers)	6,100g	Cargo
Cia. Naviera Hesperia S.A, Panama (Hadjilias and Co. Ltd.)	18,100d	Tanker
Andria Maritima S.A., Panama (Coulouthros Ltd.)	6,720g	Cargo
Scottish Tanker Co. Ltd.	16,000d	Tanker
Tramp Chartering Corp. of Panama (A. Lusi Ltd.)	18,000d	Tanker

Joseph L. Thompson & Sons Ltd., Sunderland

Albyn Line Ltd. (Allan, Black & Co., managers)	9,980d	Cargo
Hall Brothers Steamship Co. Ltd.	16,400d	Tanker
W. A. Souter & Co. Ltd.	18,000d	Tanker
South American Saint Line Ltd.	9,640d	Cargo and pass.
British Tanker Co. Ltd. (two ships)	16,000d	Tankers
Lowland Tanker Co. Ltd.	16,000d	Tanker
Sheaf Steam Shipping Co. Ltd.	18,000d	Tanker
Anglo-Saxon Petroleum Co. Ltd. (two ships)	18,000d	Tankers

Olsen & Ugelstad, Oslo	18,000d	Tanker
Westfal-Larsen and Co., A/S, Bergen	18,000d	Tanker
A/S Kollbjorg, Oslo	18,000d	Cargo
St. Helens Shipping Co. Ltd., London	26,450d	Tanker

John I. Thornycroft & Co. Ltd., Southampton

Suez Canal Co.	393g	Tug
Mersey Docks & Harbour Board	740g	Survey and buoyage
Southampton, Isle of Wight & South of England Royal Mail Steam Packet Co. Ltd. (two ships)	300g	Tugs
Peruvian Government	6,000d	Tanker
Iraq Petroleum Company	—	Launches

Vickers-Armstrongs Ltd., Barrow-in-Furness

Esso Transportation Co. Ltd.	26,600d	Tanker
Esso Petroleum Co. Ltd.	26,600d	Tanker
British Tanker Co. Ltd. (three ships)	32,000d	Tankers
Orient Steam Navigation Co. Ltd.	28,500	Pass. and cargo
Anglo-Saxon Petroleum Co. Ltd. (three ships)	18,000d	Tankers
North American Shipping and Trading Co. (London) Ltd. (S.S. Niarchos) (two ships)	44,000d	Tankers
Burmah Oil Co. (Tankers) Ltd.	32,000d	Tanker

Vickers-Armstrongs Ltd., Walker-on-Tyne

Ellerman & Bucknall Line (three ships)	13,360g	Pass. and cargo
Stavros S. Niarchos, Athens (two ships)	13,320g	Tankers
North American Shipping & Trading Co. (London) Ltd. (two ships)	20,350g	Tankers
Alfred Holt & Company	7,800g	Cargo
Esso Petroleum Co. Ltd. (two ships)	17,650g	Tankers
Alfred Holt & Company (two ships)	7,800g	Cargo and pass.
Union Steam Ship Co. of New Zealand Ltd.	8,000g	Passenger
Furness Withy & Co. Ltd.	9,450g	Cargo and pass.
Alvion Steamship Corp., Panama	20,900g	Tankers
Jorgen P. Jensen, Arendal (two ships)	16,840g	Tankers
Alfred Holt & Company (two ships)	7,800g	Cargo
Alvion Steamship Corp., Panama (two ships)	20,900g	Tankers
Ellerman Lines Ltd. (two ships)	8,480g	Cargo
Shaw, Savill & Albion Co. Ltd.	11,200g	Cargo

APPENDIX V

Extracts from the June 1959 edition of ''Merchant Ships under Construction and on Order''.

Austin & Pickersgill Ltd., Sunderland

H. Hogarth & Sons Ltd.	11,000d	Cargo
(two ships)		
W. J. Tatem Ltd.	10,000d	Cargo
Vallum Shipping Co. Ltd.	14,500d	Ore carriers
(two ships)		
Bamburgh Shipping Co. Ltd.	15,000d	Ore carriers
(two ships)		
R. S. Dalgliesh Ltd.	9,000d	Ore carrier
London & Overseas	16,000d	Cargo
Freighters Ltd (four ships)		
Manchester Liners Ltd.	6,000d	Cargo
Trader Navigation Co. Ltd.	12,000d	Cargo

Barclay, Curle & Co. Ltd., Whiteinch

Den Norske Amerikalinje, Oslo	19,700d	Tanker
Ellerman Lines	11,600d	Cargo
Watts, Watts & Co. Ltd.	11,000d	Cargo

Bartram & Sons Ltd., Sunderland

Cia. Mar. Samsoc Ltda., Panama	14,000d	Cargo
Monarch S.S. Co. Ltd.	9,900d	Cargo
Atlantic Shipping & Trading Co. Ltd.	10,000d	Cargo
Ropner Holdings Ltd.	15,500d	Cargo
Silver Line Ltd.	12,700d	Cargo
Court Line Ltd. (two ships)	11,000d	Cargo
Buries Markes Ltd.	13,500d	Cargo
New Zealand Shipping Co. Ltd.	7,500d	Refrig. cargo
Blue Star Line Ltd.	7,500d	Refrig. cargo

Blyth Dry Docks & Shipbuilding Co. Ltd., Blyth

Cory Tankers Ltd.	18,000d	Tanker
St. Denis Shipping Co. Ltd.	15,000d	Ore carriers
(four ships)		
Trader Line Ltd.	18,000d	Tanker
(Moller Line [U.K.] managers)		

Blythswood Shipbuilding Co. Ltd., Scotstoun

John I. Jacobs & Co. Ltd.	18,500d	Tanker
BP Tanker Co. Ltd.	15,500d	Tanker
Regent Petroleum Tankship Co.	19,000d	Tanker
Texas Co. (Norway) A/S, Oslo	19,000d	Tanker
H. C. Sleigh, Melbourne	27,500d	Tanker

John Brown & Co. (Clydebank) Ltd.

BP Tanker Co. Ltd.	34,500d	Tanker
BP Tanker Co. Ltd. (two ships)	65,000d	Tankers
BP Tanker Co. Ltd.	50,000d	Tanker
Union-Castle Mail S.S. Co., Ltd.	35,000g	Passenger
Clan Line Steamers Ltd.	9,800d	Cargo
(two ships)		
Federal Steam Nav. Co. Ltd.	48,500d	Tanker

Burntisland Shipbuilding Co. Ltd., Burntisland

Alexander Shipping Co. Ltd.	12,000d	Cargo
(Houlder Bros., managers)		
Power S.S. Co. Ltd.	13,600d	Cargo
Prince Line Ltd. (two ships)	5,500d	Cargo
Turnbull Scott Shipping Co. Ltd.	—	Cargo

Caledon Shipbuilding & Engineering Co. Ltd., Dundee

Athel Line Ltd. (two ships)	11,180d	Bulk carriers
Alfred Holt & Co.	9,800d	Cargo
Ellerman Lines	7,400d	Cargo

Cammell Laird & Co. (Shipbuilders & Engineers) Ltd., Birkenhead

Eagle Oil & Shipping Co. Ltd.	32,000d	Tanker
Warwick Tanker Co. Ltd.	34,500d	Tanker
Shell Tankers Ltd.	32,500d	Tanker
Shell Tankers Ltd.	60,000d	Tanker
Sugar Line Ltd.	11,250d	Bulk carrier
Union-Castle Mail S.S. Co. Ltd.	38,000d	Passenger
Bibby Line Ltd.	10,000d	Cargo
BP Tanker Co. Ltd.	65,000d	Tankers
(two ships)		

Charles Connell & Co. Ltd., Scotstoun

Scottish Ore Carriers Ltd.	9,000d	Ore carriers
(two ships)		
Wilh. Wilhelmsen, Oslo	9,000d	Cargo
Ben Line Steamers Ltd.	10,900d	Cargo
(three ships)		

William Denny & Bros. Ltd., Dumbarton

Bowater S.S. Co. Ltd.	5,400d	Cargo
Lyle Shipping Co. Ltd.	12,500d	Cargo
(two ships)		

William Doxford & Sons (Shipbuilders) Ltd., Sunderland

Sir Wm. Reardon Smith & Sons Ltd. (two ships)	10,300d	Cargo
Prince Line Ltd. (two ships)	18,500d	Tankers
Montship Lines (Buries Markes Ltd., managers)	7,000d	Cargo
T. & J. Harrison Ltd.	9,500d	Cargo
(two ships)		

Fairfield Shipbuilding & Engineering Co. Ltd., Govan

Shell Tankers Ltd. (two ships)	31,000d	Tankers
Bibby Line Ltd.	10,000d	Cargo
BP Tanker Co. Ltd.	65,000d	Tanker
BP Tanker Co. Ltd.	50,000d	Tanker
Postmaster—General	4,000g	Cable ship

Furness Shipbuilding Co. Ltd., Haverton-on-Tees

London & Overseas Freighters Ltd.	32,000d Tanker
Andria Maritima S.A., Panama	18,200d Tanker
Soc. Transoceanica Canopus S.A., Panama (two ships)	15,900d Cargo
Eagle Tanker Co. Ltd. (two ships)	32,000d Tankers
Shell Tankers Ltd.	31,000d Tanker
Hunting & Son Ltd.	18,000d Tanker
Gulf Oil Corp., U.S.A. (four ships)	40,000d Tankers
Trent Maritime Co. Ltd.	15,900d Cargo
Trent Maritime Co. Ltd.	24,650d Tanker
John I. Jacobs & Co. Ltd.	18,200d Tanker
British Oil Shipping Co. Ltd. (three ships)	25,500d Tankers
British Oil Shipping Co. Ltd.	18,000d Tanker

William Gray & Co. Ltd., West Hartlepool

N. G. Livanos, Greece	12,000d Cargo
Ore Carriers Ltd. (two ships)	14,300d Ore carriers
Irish Shipping Ltd.	9,500d Cargo
Guinea Gulf Line Ltd.	8,000d Cargo

Greenock Dockyard Co. Ltd., Greenock

Union-Castle Mail S.S. Co. Ltd. (two ships)	10,100d Refrig. cargo
Clan Line Steamers Ltd. (two ships)	10,000d Cargo

Hall, Russell & Co. Ltd., Aberdeen

Burnett S.S. Co. Ltd.	6,500d Cargo
Pacific Steam Nav. Co.	7,000d Cargo

William Hamilton & Co. Ltd., Port Glasgow

Hain S.S. Co. Ltd.	10,000d Cargo
T. & J. Brocklebank Ltd.	10,400d Cargo
Th. Brovig, Farsund	19,000d Tanker
H. Kuhnle's Rederi, Bergen	10,800d Cargo
Hector Atlantic Ltd.	19,000d Tanker
Tonsbergs Hvalfangeri, Tonsberg	13,500d Cargo
Cunard S.S. Co. Ltd. (two ships)	7,000g Cargo
BP Tanker Co. Ltd.	15,500d Tanker

Harland & Wolff Ltd., Belfast

BP Tanker Co. Ltd.	42,000d Tanker
British Oil Shipping Co. Ltd.	46,000d Tanker
BP Tanker Co. Ltd.	14,000d Tanker
Royal Mail Lines Ltd. (three ships)	20,000g Passenger
Skibs A/S Dalfonn, Stavanger	12,500d Cargo
Belships Co. A/S, Oslo	15,500d Cargo
P.&O. S.N. Co.	45,000g Passenger
Reidar Rod, Tonsberg	25,000d Tanker
Olav Ringdal, Oslo	25,000d Tanker
Shaw Savill Line	11,000g Refrig. cargo
Pacific Stm. Nav. Co.	28,300d Tanker
Pacific Stm. Nav. Co.	46,400d Tanker
Port Line Ltd. (two ships)	— Refrig. cargo
BP Tanker Co. Ltd. (three ships)	50,000d Tankers
BP Tanker Co. Ltd. (three ships)	15,500d Tankers
Halfdan Ditlev Simonsen, Oslo	9,300d Cargo
Lorentzen's Rederi, Oslo	9,500d Cargo
Bank Line Ltd. (two ships)	12,000d Cargo
Bank Line Ltd. (four ships)	10,270d Cargo

Harland & Wolff Ltd., Govan

Hunting & Son Ltd.	28,350d Tanker
BP Tanker Co. Ltd.	14,000d Tanker
British India S.N. Co. Ltd. (four ships)	6,500d Cargo
Belships Co. A/S, Oslo	12,500d Cargo
Sigval Bergesen, Stavanger	17,000d Tanker
BP Tanker Co. Ltd.	15,500d Tanker
Lorentzen's Rederi, Oslo (two ships)	12,500d Cargo
Mil Tankrederi, Oslo	15,000d Tanker

Hawthorn, Leslie (Shipbuilders) Ltd., Hebburn

Moor Line Ltd.	10,000d Cargo
BP Tanker Co. Ltd. (three ships)	34,500d Tankers
Moor Line Ltd.	11,800d Cargo
Houlder Line Ltd. (two ships)	10,300d Refrig. cargo
"K" S.S. Co. Ltd.	43,750d Tanker
Athel Line Ltd.	18,000d Tanker
Warwick Tanker Co. Ltd.	34,500d Tanker
Hadley Shipping Co. Ltd.	18,000d Tanker

Sir James Laing & Sons Ltd., Sunderland

Sheaf Stm. Shpg. Co. Ltd.	15,000d Ore carrier
Wm. Cory & Son Ltd.	20,000d Tanker
A/S Tanktransport, Tonsberg	20,000d Tanker
John I. Jacobs & Co. Ltd.	32,000d Tanker
Thorvald Berg, Tonsberg	14,500d Cargo

Lithgows Ltd., Port Glasgow

Charlton Stm. Shpg. Co. Ltd.	14,000d Ore carrier
BP Tanker Co. Ltd. (two ships)	15,500d Tankers
N. R. Bugge, Tonsberg	19,000d Tanker
Crest Shipping Co. Ltd.	11,300d Cargo
Lyle Shipping Co. Ltd. (two ships)	15,000d Ore carriers
BP Tanker Co. Ltd.	34,500d Tanker
British & Burmese S.N. Co. Ltd. (two ships)	10,200d Cargo
H. Clarkson & Co. Ltd.	12,700d Cargo
Jamaica Banana Producers S.S. Co. Ltd.	5,280d Refrig. cargo
Asiatic S.N. Co. Ltd.	11,600d Cargo

John Readhead & Sons Ltd., South Shields

H. Hogarth & Sons Ltd.	11,000d Cargo
Wm. France Fenwick & Co. Ltd.	10,500d Bulk carrier
Hain S.S. Co. Ltd.	10,300d Cargo
Strick Line Ltd.	13,000d Cargo

Scotts' Shipbuilding & Engineering Co. Ltd., Greenock

Elder Dempster Lines Ltd. (two ships)	9,650d Cargo
British India S.N. Co. Ltd.	19,100d Tanker
BP Tanker Co. Ltd.	14,000d Tanker
Vallum Shipping Co. Ltd. (two ships)	14,500d Ore carriers

Short Brothers Ltd., Sunderland

Niarchos (London) Ltd. (two ships)	14,100d Cargo
Nomikos (London) Ltd.	14,100d Cargo
S. M. Kuhnle & Son, Bergen	13,890d Cargo
S. Ditlev-Simonsen, Oslo	13,900d Cargo
Chapman & Willan Ltd. (three ships)	11,000d Cargo
B. J. Hanssen, Flekkefjord	13,900d Cargo

Smith's Dock Co. Ltd., South Bank-on-Tees

Shell Tankers Ltd.	18,000d Tanker
Charter Shipping Co.,	
Bermuda (P.&O.)	18,000d Tankers
(two ships)	
BP Tanker Co. Ltd.	15,500d Tanker
A/S Uglands Rederi, Grimstad	13,500d Cargo
(two ships)	
Bolton S.S. Co. Ltd.	12,500d Cargo
Northern Petroleum Tank S.S. Co.	15,500d Ore carrier
Lowland Tanker Co. Ltd.	19,000d Tankers
(two ships)	
Turnbull Scott Shipping Co. Ltd.	18,000d Tanker

Alexander Stephen & Sons Ltd., Linthouse

Ellerman Lines	11,000d Cargo
BP Tanker Co. Ltd.	14,000d Tanker
Shaw Savill Line	11,000g Refrig. cargo
Elder Dempster Lines Ltd.	10,000d Cargo
Avenue Shipping Co. Ltd.	9,900d Cargo
Mobil Oil Co. Ltd. (two ships)	19,000d Tankers
BP Tanker Co. Ltd.	50,000d Tanker
Elders & Fyffes Ltd.	— Refrig. cargo
(two ships)	
Lamport & Holt Line Ltd.	— Refrig. cargo

Swan, Hunter & Wigham Richardson Ltd., Wallsend-on-Tyne

Shell Tankers Ltd.	65,000d Tanker
BP Tanker Co. Ltd.	42,000d Tanker
British India S.N. Co. Ltd.	37,000d Tankers
(two ships)	
Helmer Staubo & Co., Oslo	38,000d Tanker
Port Line Ltd.	13,000d Refrig. cargo
BP Tanker Co. Ltd. (two ships)	65,000d Tanker
British & Commonwealth	— Refrig.
Shipping Co. Ltd.	cargo

Neptune Works, Walker-on-Tyne

Palm Line Ltd. (two ships)	8,550d Cargo
Cia. Nacional de Nav., Lisbon	20,000g Pass./cargo
Furness Houlder Argentine Lines	19,000d Tanker
Lowland Tanker Co. Ltd.	18,000d Tanker

Joseph L. Thompson & Sons Ltd., Sunderland

BP Tanker Co. Ltd.	34,500d Tanker
Bamburgh Shipping Co. Ltd.	18,000d Ore carrier
South American Saint Line	9,500d Cargo
(two ships)	
Silver Line Ltd.	11,600d Cargo
BP Tanker Co. Ltd. (two ships)	50,000d Tankers
Shell Tankers Ltd. (two ships)	18,000d Tankers

Vickers-Armstrongs (Shipbuilders) Ltd., Barrow-in-Furness

BP Tanker Co. Ltd.	42,000d Tanker
Orient S.N. Co. Ltd.	40,000g Passenger
BP Tanker Co. Ltd. (three ships)	50,000d Tankers

Vickers-Armstrongs (Shipbuilders) Ltd., Walker-on-Tyne

Shaw Savill Line	11,500g Refrig. cargo
Shell Tankers Ltd.	65,000d Tanker
Alfred Holt & Co.	9,650d Cargo
Orient S.N. Co. Ltd.	37,000d Tanker
Esso Petroleum Co. Ltd.	30,150g Tankers
(two ships)	
Canadian Pacific	27,500g Passenger
Steamships Ltd.	
Ellerman Lines (two ships)	8,200g Cargo
Overseas owners	— Tanker
